Modern Signalling HANDBOOK

5th Edition

Chris Hall

First published 2016

ISBN 978 07110 3839 4

Published by Ian Allan Publishing Ltd, Addlestone, Surrey KT15 2SF.

Printed in Wales

Visit the Ian Allan Publishing website at www.ianallanpublishing.com

Contents

Preface

The fourth edition of *Modern Signalling Handbook* was published in 2010 under the authorship of my father, Stanley Hall MBE. Since then there have been several major changes to signalling technology, in particular the implementation of Rail Operating Centres, the GSM-R radio system, modular signalling and manually controlled level crossings with obstacle detection. The European Train Control System has also been installed on the former Cambrian lines and will soon be in service on the Thameslink route. The opportunity has therefore been taken to completely update the fourth edition with new material and photographs as appropriate. It should be noted that reference to specific sections of the Rule Book has been removed from this edition as updating of this publication soon renders such references out of date. The up-to-date Rule Book can be accessed on the internet at www.rssb.co.uk. The final section of the book is a list of technical terms and abbreviations; each term is italicised when first mentioned in the main text of the book.

I am grateful to my father for providing much of the source material for this edition of *Modern Signalling Handbook* from the fourth edition, and to a former colleague, Stuart Johnson, for his contribution. I hope that the book continues to be of value in providing a useful introduction to the subject of signalling on the main-line British railway network.

Signalling on London Underground and light rail systems is outside the scope of this book.

Chris Hall
CEng, FIRSE, MIMechE, CMIOSH
Derby
June 2016

PART 1

CHAPTER 1

Historical development of signalling in the 19th century

If trains always ran on time and never broke down, there would be little need for a signalling system. The timetable could be devised so that the trains would always be a safe distance apart. This was the philosophy in the early days of railways and it worked quite well so long as trains were few and speeds were low. Even though breakdowns were frequent, the guards had time to go back along the line showing a red flag or lamp to warn the driver of the next train about the obstruction in front of him.

However, as the railway age developed and trains became both faster and more frequent, the need for some system of keeping them apart, of preventing them from crashing into each other, quickly became apparent. The first signalling methods were based on a time-interval philosophy. Trains were not allowed to leave or pass a station until a predetermined time had elapsed since the previous train had left, and the necessary instructions were given to the driver in one of two ways – either by hand signal or by fixed signal. A policeman appointed for the purpose by the railway company gave hand signals, and he gave his message to the driver by holding his arms in various positions. At some stations, wooden posts were erected, bearing various forms of movable equipment that could be operated by the policeman to give the various messages. These wooden post signals became known as fixed signals because they were literally fixed in the ground in a predetermined position. The first semaphore signal was erected by the South Eastern Railway at New Cross in 1841. Most of today's trains are still controlled by fixed signals, although shunting movements are dealt with by both fixed and hand signals; the exceptions are lines with *cab signalling*. The time-interval signalling system had fundamental shortcomings. As traffic levels grew it became necessary to run trains at more frequent intervals, and if a train broke down the guard had little time to run back showing his danger signal. A more serious problem arose when a train proceeded slowly for some reason and was thus in danger of being run into by a following faster train. This type of collision became known as an 'overtaking accident', with a meaning quite different from its use when applied to road traffic today.

It soon became clear that a much greater standard of safety could be achieved if a train was not allowed to leave a station until it was known that the previous train had arrived safely at the next station, and fortunately a means of allowing this to be done had just been devised – the electric telegraph. This equipment first appeared in the 1840s and led to the development of what became known as the absolute block system. This was based on the principle that safety could be achieved if the line was divided into a series of sections (or blocks), with a policeman (or signalman as he was becoming known) at the end of each section. Under this system, no train is allowed to enter the section until the previous train has left it. This principle was described in the following terms: 'the object of absolute block signalling is to prevent more than one train being in a block section on the same line at the same time.'

The term 'absolute' refers to the absolute prohibition of there being more than one train in a block section at the same time. The term 'block' then began to take on a more general meaning, embracing any signalling system worked by electric telegraph between signalmen in adjacent signal boxes, and is still in use today to describe the system employed in the most recently signalled areas, called *track circuit block*.

The early fixed signals were operated from the foot of the signal post, but it was soon realised that it would be more efficient if signals could be operated from a distance by pulling a wire, and it became the practice to concentrate the operation of signals (and subsequently points) in one place, which became known as a

ABOVE An interior view of Edington Junction signal box on the Bridgwater Railway in Somerset, as opened in 1890. The Bridgwater Railway ran to Bridgwater from Edington Junction, on the Somerset & Dorset Joint Railway's Highbridge to Glastonbury line. *Stuart Johnson*

'signal box'. It then became possible to interlock the levers working the points and signals so that a driver could not be shown signals that conflicted with the routes that had been set. The first such interlocking was installed at Bricklayers Arms, on the South Eastern Railway, in 1843.

The essentials of a safe and efficient signalling system were now in place:

1. The concentration of control of points and signals in a signal box
2. The interlocking of points and signals
3. Electric telegraphic communication between adjacent signal boxes
4. The absolute block signalling system and the regulations for its operation

The absolute block system was installed throughout Britain during the second half of the 19th century (its use on lines used by passenger trains was mandated by the Regulation of Railways Act 1889) and it was gradually refined by the adoption of a variety of technical measures mainly designed to overcome the problem of human error on the part of signalmen. Human error is a general term covering unconscious or unwitting acts, such as a lack of attention or concentration; impulsive but erroneous reactions; errors committed under pressure; and just plain forgetfulness. It recognises that human beings are not infallible, and if the travelling public is to be safeguarded against the possibly calamitous effects of human error by signalmen, it is advantageous to adopt all the safeguards that the advances in science and technology can provide. These advances were almost always won the hard way, as a result of lessons learned from accidents, and the learning process has never stopped. It was difficult to justify the cost of installing the complete range of safeguards at every signal box, so the busier signal boxes were better protected than those that were quieter and situated on less important routes.

The braking systems in use on trains during most of the 19th century were primitive and inadequate, and as trains became faster and heavier, drivers found it increasingly difficult to stop safely if the signals were against them (i.e. at danger). An auxiliary signal was therefore devised, situated several hundred yards before a *stop signal*, in order to give the driver prior warning of the need to stop if a signal was at danger. This auxiliary signal became known by the term *distant signal* and originally drivers were expected to stop at it if it was at danger. The impracticality of this was eventually recognised and the distant signal came to be regarded as a warning or caution signal, giving the driver prior indication of the state of the stop signal ahead.

Many accidents occurred because drivers found themselves unable to stop in time at a stop signal showing danger, even after having been warned by the distant signal. They ran past the stop signal, or *home signal*, and into collision with a train or vehicles standing just beyond it. To avoid such collisions, the concept of an *overlap*, set at a quarter of a mile (440 yards/400 metres), was adopted. Henceforth the signalman did not send the 'train out of section' message to his colleague at the previous signal box until the rear of the train had passed such a distance beyond the home signal. This safety overlap became known as the 'quarter of a mile clearance', and the far end of the overlap became known as the *clearing point*. In later years, when colour-light distant signals came into use, the greater visibility of these signals enabled the clearing point to be reduced to 200 yards (180 metres).

The use of the quarter of a mile clearance was unduly restrictive at some places, and a regulation was devised, universally known as 'Regulation 5' (because it was the fifth regulation in the signalling regulations book). This authorised signalmen at specified locations to allow a train to proceed towards their signal box from the previous one, with a train or vehicles occupying their quarter of a mile clearance. The driver was advised, by fixed or hand signal, or verbally, that he was being allowed to proceed under the *warning arrangement* (Regulation 5), and he was expected to approach the next signal box cautiously. This regulation originally applied to both passenger and freight trains, but in later years its use was confined to freight trains.

The use of the absolute block system was confined mainly to double- and multiple-*track* lines used by passenger trains. For lines used only by freight trains, a system known as *permissive block working* came into use, which allowed more than one train to be in a block section at the same time. There were no overlaps, and the driver of a train being admitted to a section of line still *occupied* by the previous train was advised of the fact by the use of signals or verbally. The driver was expected to travel slowly enough to be able to stop safely if he caught up with the train in front. Lower standards of safety were accepted in the operation of freight trains than with passenger trains. Permissive block for passenger trains was often introduced at larger passenger stations to enable a train to enter a platform line already occupied by another train, but such movements were made at low speed and over short distances and were therefore reasonably safe.

The development of signalling on single lines had progressed in a similar manner to that on double lines. At first there was no system other than the timetable; then the electric telegraph came into use for passing messages regulating the passage of trains over single lines between stations. Misunderstandings led to several accidents, and the electric telegraph system was refined by adapting it to control the issue of *tokens*. These were handed to drivers and gave them authority to enter the single-line section. The tokens were contained in token machines kept in each signal box or station, and the machines at each end of a section were electrically interlocked with each other so that only one token for a section could be out at any one time. Fixed signals were also used and the system became known as the *electric token block* system, which is described in more detail in Chapter 28.

A system sometimes used on quieter single lines was known as the *staff and ticket* system. A box of tickets was kept in each signal box or station, and could only be unlocked by a key on the end of the train staff (a wooden or metal rod engraved with the name of the section of line along which its possession authorised the driver to take his train). There was only one staff for each section and trains could only be admitted to a single-line section from the end where the staff lay. If a train was to be followed by another one, the driver of the first train was given a ticket and shown the staff. The driver of the last train through the section in one direction was given the staff. It was a cheap and simple system, but it could lead to delays if the staff happened to be at the wrong end of the section.

On single lines used by only one train, such as short dead-end branches, a very simple system came into use, known as 'one engine in steam'. A single-line staff, usually a wooden or metal rod, engraved with the name of the branch, was the driver's authority to enter the single line, and as there was only one such staff in existence, safety was assured.

By the end of the 19th century British railway signalling had evolved into a potentially very safe system, and henceforth its development was to be in a different direction. At that time, the railways were very busy, and much thought began to be directed towards ways of improving efficiency and reducing costs. The number of signal boxes needed was determined partly by the distance over which a signalman could operate points (finally set at 350 yards/320 metres, but less at that time), partly by the workload, and partly by the size of the area that the signalman could control visually. One of the problems in busy areas was the large number of signal boxes required in the conditions then existing. In such circumstances it was very difficult to keep signalmen fully informed of the nature and timing of train movements approaching them so that they could make the best decisions about the priority of any particular movement. There was often insufficient time for signalmen to consult one another about proposed movements, and the overall result was unnecessary delay to trains on the one hand, and wasted line or platform capacity on the other.

Fortunately, as had happened previously, a technical solution was available – the application of electric or pneumatic power to the operation of points and signals – and several large power-operated signal boxes came into use in the few years before the First World War. The first electro-pneumatic installation was at Bishopsgate (Great Eastern Railway), in 1898; and in 1900 the London & North Western Railway installed an all-electric signal box at Crewe. Although the absolute block system was still used, it had to be considerably modified at large stations. In other areas the use of power-operated points and *track circuits* (an electrically operated train detection device) enabled two or three signal boxes to be combined into one, but the cost of such schemes limited their application. In Britain, track circuits were first used in 1894 in Gas Works Tunnel, just outside London King's Cross station.

Developments between the First and Second World Wars consisted mainly of the further application of existing safety devices and economy measures. However, the birth of modern signalling, based on continuous track circuiting, *multiple-aspect colour light signals*, and *route setting* of points and signals by a single switch, with the interlocking being achieved by electrical relays, belongs to that period, and its development is the subject of the second chapter.

CHAPTER 2

Historical development of signalling in the 20th century

The landmarks in the development of signalling that were considered in the previous chapter are:

1. The concentration in one place (the signal box) of the operation of all the points and signals in an area, and their interlocking
2. The use of various block signalling systems
3. The application of power (electrical, pneumatic or hydraulic) to the operation of points and signals, enabling more concentration to take place
4. The invention of the track circuit, which detects the presence (or more accurately, the absence) of a train

In this chapter the story is taken forward to the signalling control centres, known as *Integrated Electronic Control Centres* (IECCs). These have their genesis on the East Coast Main Line at Thirsk and Northallerton where, shortly before the Second World War, the London & North Eastern Railway (LNER) introduced a new system known as *route relay interlocking*, in which the interlocking between points and signals is achieved by electrical relays. These allowed the signaller (the modern day term for signalman will be used from this point) to set the points and clear the signal for the desired route merely by turning a switch. On open stretches of line between stations and junctions the signals worked automatically, turning to red (danger) as soon as a train passed them, then to yellow (caution) and two yellows (preliminary caution), and finally to green as the train went on its way and passed further signals.

The first daylight signals were installed by the Liverpool Overhead Railway in 1919. In London, the District and Metropolitan railways, which later became part of London Underground, had installed *colour light signals* as early as 1905, but only in tunnels, as they lacked the optical power necessary for use in daylight. *Three-aspect* colour light signals were first installed between Marylebone and Neasden, on the LNER, in 1923 and, in a subsequent development to allow trains to operate at closer *headways*, *four-aspect* colour light signals were introduced between Holborn Viaduct and Elephant & Castle on the Southern Railway in 1926.

The Thirsk and Northallerton schemes allowed signallers to control a far greater area than previously, much of it beyond the signaller's view. So that a signaller could know what was going on in those

LEFT The operating floor of the 1936 Waterloo signal box showing the power lever frame and miniature levers to operate the signalling equipment. There were 309 levers in total split into three different sections. The box remained in use until 1984. *IAL*

RIGHT A June 1939 view of the interior of London Victoria Eastern signal box, when the signalling was converted to colour lights, showing the pistol-grip slides for operating the equipment. *IAL*

areas out of sight, a large *signalling panel* giving a geographical representation of the track layout and signals, etc, in the box's area was provided. In the Northallerton signal box, a series of white electric lights on the panel showed which way the routes were set, as well as (by red lights) the location of trains within a section, and whether signals had been cleared for trains to proceed. The signaller had to remember which trains they were, to set the correct route, and give the appropriate priority at junctions. As the areas controlled from one signal box became larger, or more complex, a system of showing in the signal box a train's description or identity was devised. The indicators showing this were appropriately called *train describers*.

Signal boxes of the Thirsk/Northallerton type were known as *route setting* or *one control switch* (OCS) installations, because there was one route or control switch for each route at a junction. A refinement of the OCS method was the *NX* system, first introduced at Brunswick near Liverpool in 1937.

The letters NX stand for *entrance/exit*, in which a route is set by pressing a button or turning a switch at the start of (or entrance to) a route and pressing another button at the end of (or exit from) that route. This simplified the signaller's operating equipment and enabled the operating push-buttons (or switches) to be incorporated on the panel itself.

One of the most significant developments in the 1960s was the development of *remote control systems* to allow the power signalling of large areas. In most large signal boxes using route-relay interlocking, the interlocking equipment controls only those points and signals within the immediate vicinity. The interlocking of points and signals that are further away is usually dealt with in outlying installations, housed in buildings known as *remote interlockings*, each one dealing with a station or junction area. Communication between the main signal box and the remote interlockings is typically by *time division multiplex* (TDM) through a cable that is either housed in concrete troughing at the lineside or buried at a shallow depth.

ABOVE The 1955-built signal box at Llandilo (now Llandeilo), on the Central Wales Line, replaced the North and South boxes. The signal box controlled the junction with the line to Carmarthen. *IAL*

Around this time, the development of *train describers* occurred in which the *train descriptions* are shown on the panel by train description numbers, each in a position corresponding to the actual location of the train in a particular section of track. Every train has a four-digit identity number, e.g. 1A20, the first digit being the class of train (class 1 is an express passenger train); the letter representing the route or destination area (e.g. A=destination London); and the third and fourth digits the serial number of the train or service. The train description number is shown in the train describer panel next to the signal that the train is approaching, and as the train passes that signal and proceeds towards the next one the train description number automatically steps forwards to be displayed in the next signal section.

The development of manually controlled full barrier level crossings that could be operated remotely under CCTV supervision allowed gate boxes to be closed, and the operation of this type of crossing to be concentrated in the signal box.

Remote control, train describers and supervision of full barrier crossings by CCTV led to the

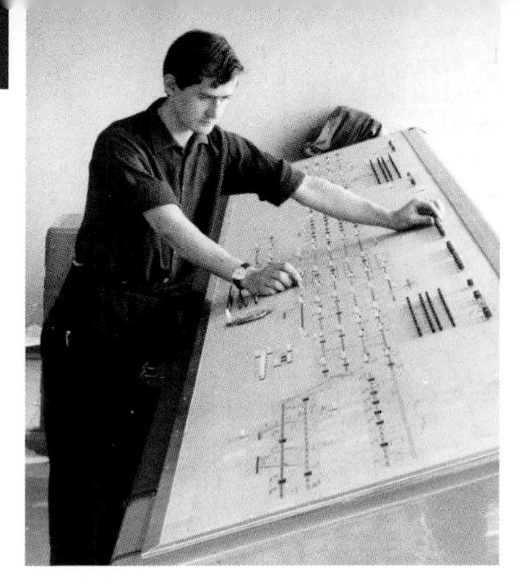

ABOVE A 1966 view of the entrance-exit (NX) panel in the panel box at Basingstoke. Commissioned in 1966, the box remained in use until 2007. *IAL*

ABOVE The operating floor at Derby power signal box, opened in 1969, showing the typical entrance/exit (NX) panel of the period. While still currently in use, its area will be taken over during the next few years by the new Derby Rail Operating Centre (known as the East Midlands Control Centre) located nearby. *Author*

commissioning of very large combined control and indications panels. These large panels required the signaller to walk to and fro to operate the push-buttons, and in some signal boxes the panel functions were split so that the signaller could sit and operate the push-buttons on a console in the form of a miniature replica panel, with all the signal, route, track circuit, etc, indications being shown on a larger, separate panel.

These very large signal boxes became standardised during the 1960s and 1970s and controlled most main lines and large stations. Technically there was no limit to the area that could be supervised and controlled from one signal box, and natural development resulted in some very large installations such as those at London Bridge and Victoria, each employing many signallers per shift. The name 'signal box' was felt to be inappropriate for these modern installations and they became 'signalling centres', although the designation 'power signal box', or PSB for short, remained in common use.

Until quite recently the basis of all power signalling installations was the *track circuit*, a simple piece of equipment that feeds a weak electric current through a section of track electrically insulated from the adjoining sections. When the wheels of a train pass on to the section of track concerned they short-circuit the current, causing a relay to de-energise, which in turn controls other operations, e.g. placing signals to danger, locking points, transferring train descriptions on the signaller's panel, or *visual display unit* (VDU) screen, from signal to signal, etc. All the *running lines* (i.e. all lines other than sidings) are track-circuited throughout their length, and signals are erected at conventional intervals, based upon the distance a train needs to stop from the driver seeing the first cautionary aspect while travelling at full speed. Each signal is capable of showing at least three aspects: a red light, a yellow light or a green light. In busy areas, or on busy high-speed lines, signals can also display an additional yellow light to form a *double yellow aspect*. This acts as a preliminary caution with the following signal displaying a cautionary single *yellow aspect* at that time.

Track circuits are prone to *rightside failure,* which puts signals to danger and causes delay. In more recent years, much greater use has been made of *axle counters*, such as on the West Coast Main Line and in areas where track circuits are especially prone to failure, e.g. in wet tunnels and on stretches of line affected by salt water spray. Axle-counting equipment counts the number of axles on a train passing over the counting head into a section of line, and similar equipment at the far end of the section counts them out of the section. If the two counts agree, the section is considered clear.

The major development in signalling control was the Integrated Electronic Control Centre (IECC), brought about by changes in traffic patterns and technology. The first one was commissioned at London Liverpool Street at Easter 1989 and was quickly followed by IECCs at York and Yoker (Glasgow). The pattern of train services today is much more stable, predictable and repetitive than it used to be. Passenger train timetables are now generally based on a regular and repeating service pattern; cancellations, special trains and other deviations from the train plan are relatively infrequent. Freight trains are infrequently seen on many routes.

A typical IECC is likely to contain the following features, which distinguish it from the previous generation of power signal boxes:

1. A stable and predictable train service pattern, which can be downloaded into a computer
2. *Automatic route setting* (ARS), by means of which the route at a junction is selected by the computer based on the train description number of an approaching train and a certain amount of priority logic, previously programmed, thus relieving the signaller of repetitive tasks
3. Computer-driven train describer equipment, which operates the signaller's train describers, and acts as an information base for the dissemination of train running information, public address announcements, the operation of train departure indicators, etc, and for record purposes
4. Several visual display units (VDUs), replacing the signaller's operating/indications panel, and requiring much less space
5. A change in the method by which the signaller operates points and signals; instead of using push-buttons he enters his commands by keyboard or trackerball
6. The interlocking between points and signals, instead of being carried out by banks of electrical relays, is dealt with by a computer software program in conjunction with solid state electronic equipment. This requires much less space; hence the IECC can be housed in a much smaller building than a 1960s/1970s power signal box.

The role of the signaller in an IECC contrasts markedly with that of his colleague in a traditional manually operated signal box. In an IECC the signaller controls train movements over a very large area and is able to do this because:

1. Commands can be entered quickly and easily
2. Automatic route setting lightens the workload
3. The visual information about trains, their description and disposition, which is readily available, enables the signaller to determine priorities and make train regulating decisions quickly and to the best advantage
4. Safety, which is a major preoccupation of a signaller in a *manual signal box*, is largely incorporated into the signalling system equipment itself. In normal circumstances, an IECC signaller cannot move points dangerously, nor give a 'clear' (proceed) signal to a driver when it is unsafe to do so. The signaller can therefore concentrate on train regulating decisions without the heavy and physically tiring work of the signaller in a manual signal box.

The stages in the development of signalling technology in the 50 years between the *route relay interlocking* signal box at Northallerton and an IECC have been as follows:

1. Introduction of the large power signal box, facilitated by the development of remote control systems, with routes being set on the entrance/exit principle by push-button or switch
2. The incorporation of train descriptions into the illuminated diagram panel

RIGHT The operating floor and entrance/exit (NX) panel at the busy Birmingham New Street power signal box opened in 1966 to control train movements in the immediate New Street station area. This will be taken over by the new West Midlands Rail Operating Centre at Saltley in due course. *Author*

LEFT A later generation of power signal box using relays and with an entrance/exit (NX) panel is shown here at Westbury, opened in 1984. *RAIB*

3. Automatic route setting
4. The replacement of the large diagram panel by visual display units
5. Computer-driven train describer equipment
6. The replacement of relays by solid state electronic equipment in the interlocking

On single lines in areas controlled by power signal boxes, it has been quite simple to convert the electric token block system to track circuit block, but in more remote areas electric token block generally reigned supreme until well after the Second World War. In order to simplify operation, however, a system known as *tokenless block* was introduced, in which the use of a token to guarantee that there would only be one train in a single-line section at the same time was replaced by a system of sequential track circuit occupation and clearance to prove that a train had passed through a section before a further train could be admitted from either end. The tokenless block system is described in more detail in Chapter 28.

Economic necessity led to the development in the 1980s of the *Radio Electronic Token Block* system (RETB) for controlling long rural single lines in Scotland, Wales and East Anglia that were previously signalled using traditional manual signal boxes. It achieved its economy by eliminating the need for the intermediate signal boxes and lineside cabling, since all train movements are controlled by radio from a central point. RETB is based in principle on the well-tried electric token block system, the differences being:

1. Instead of the signaller handing the driver a physical token, an electronic 'token' is issued to the driver by radio, and appears on an instrument in the driving cab, the names of the ends of the section concerned being displayed in a window in the instrument.
2. There are no lineside signals, merely marker boards, and all instructions to the driver are given by radio by the signaller.
3. Hydro-pneumatic points at crossing loops. A points indicator (a yellow aspect) is provided to confirm that the points are correctly set and detected for trains entering the loop. Trains leaving the loop in the opposite direction can 'trail' through the points without damaging them. In recent years, these points have been converted to more conventional power operation as described in Chapter 28.
4. The *Train Protection and Warning System (TPWS)* (described in more detail in Chapter 23) has been provided as a later enhancement to the RETB system. A blue flashing light mounted on the same post as a stop board indicates to the driver that the *electronic token* has been transmitted and the TPWS will not intervene when the train passes the stop board.

British railway signalling is technically very advanced, and its development might be thought of as a series of steps rather than a gradual smooth process. Although much of Britain's railway system is signalled by modern methods, there still remain hundreds of miles controlled by traditional systems born in the 19th century, together with a number of signal boxes that represent intermediate stages of development. These are, however, gradually disappearing under Network Rail's policy of concentrating signalling control in new Rail Operating Centres, as described in the next chapter.

If the railways are to be operated safely it is not enough for the signalling system to be modern and foolproof. It is also essential that the message given by the signal arm or light is observed, correctly interpreted and correctly acted upon by the driver. The interface between signal and driver is vital, and the penalty for error is severe. Before the end of the 19th century several railway companies were developing forms of cab signalling to give audible warning to drivers and reinforce the visual message given by the signal. The North Eastern Railway pioneered the introduction of *Automatic Train Control* (ATC), but only on a small scale, and its installation was discontinued by the London & North Eastern Railway after the 1923 Grouping of railway companies into the 'Big Four'. The only system that was developed and installed on a large scale was the Great Western's ATC, though the London Midland & Scottish Railway had a small-scale installation of the *Hudd system* on its London, Tilbury & Southend line. Both systems warned the driver that he was about to pass a distant signal at caution, and both caused the brakes to be applied if the driver failed to acknowledge the warning. After nationalisation in 1948, the railways started to develop a modification of the Hudd system, which became known as the BR *Automatic Warning System* (BR-AWS). Installation started in 1958 and continued over many years, often in parallel with *power signal box* resignalling schemes, until the whole network was fitted. AWS is described in more detail in Chapter 22.

AWS is a fairly simple system, mainly advisory, and although it has been valuable in reducing the number of collisions it has two serious drawbacks:

1. The audible warning does not differentiate between signals showing two yellows, one yellow, or red, which is a situation that could mislead a driver.
2. AWS does not monitor the driver's response to a warning to see that he is braking correctly.

For these reasons, in 1988 BR considered adopting a system known as *Automatic Train Protection* (ATP) (Chapter 24), and trials were carried out on two routes from London (the Great Western and Chiltern lines). However, the trials were prolonged with many problems that had to be solved before a workable system was in place. Ultimately it was considered that further fitment of ATP was likely to be too expensive to be cost effective. The Government, on the advice of British Rail, therefore decided in 1994 not to extend the ATP system to other routes.

However, the decision not to proceed with the fitment of ATP left the railways no better protected against the consequences of driver error than before. It was therefore essential that the defects of BR-AWS were remedied as soon as possible in view of the time that had passed while ATP was being tried. The selected solution was the Train Protection and Warning System (TPWS), which provides a speed trap on the approach to, and a trip stop at, selected signals that can show a red aspect. The signals selected are those where there are points and crossings in the line ahead at which conflicting movements could occur, or those that have been specially identified as being at a higher risk of being passed at danger. The speed trap has the capability of being effective at speeds up to 120km/h (75mph), and is designed to brake a train that it detects as travelling too fast to a stop, within the overlap of the signal, i.e. before reaching a point where it might encounter another train. The fitment of an additional speed trap can extend the protection up to 160km/h (100mph) (known as *TPWS+*). The trip stop will immediately apply the brakes on any train passing the signal when it is at danger.

By the end of the 20th century the signalling industry – indeed, the railway industry as a whole – was on the verge of a major step forward in the long history of signalling and train control. European Union directives require European railways, including those in Britain, to adopt a common system known as the *European Rail Traffic Management System* (ERTMS). This has a number of features, some of them revolutionary, among which are a standard ATP system; the possible abolition of lineside signals; train position being reported by radio using transponders instead of track circuits or axle counters; and instructions, *movement authorities*, to drivers being given by radio. ERTMS is described in more detail in Chapter 26.

BELOW The operating panel in Westbury power signal box. In this case, the buttons for setting routes are not mounted in the main panel but in separate desk-mounted extracts from the panel as shown. *RAIB*

CHAPTER 3

Signalling developments in the 21st century

At the present time signalling is very much in a state of transition, as has been the case for very many years. There are still significant pockets of absolute block signalling remaining, but these are declining rapidly. The big power signal boxes of the 1960s and 1970s, in which the signalling is controlled using route relay interlocking, are mostly still there, but they are gradually being replaced by new signalling centres. There have been some notable closures, such as Leicester, dating from the 1980s, and Trent, from the late 1960s.

The capacity of telecommunications systems is now such that there is no longer any technical constraint on the size of an area that can be controlled by one control centre. Network Rail's strategy (in 2016) is therefore to control the entire network from 12 Rail Operating Centres (ROCs). These are planned for the following places:

- Basingstoke
- Cardiff
- Derby
- Didcot
- Edinburgh
- Glasgow
- Gillingham
- Manchester
- Romford
- Rugby
- Three Bridges
- York

To achieve this, much existing signalling is simply being recontrolled using the existing relay and solid state interlockings. Thus, although a route may be controlled from one of the new ROCs, the equipment at the trackside may well remain the same, other than changes of, for example, signal identification plates.

A typical ROC is a very large modern building containing a number of signaller workstations, each supervising a specific area of railway. Visual display screens now form the standard signaller interface for controlling/supervising the signalling equipment, and there are usually four or more screens for this purpose. Automatic route setting is also likely to be provided.

As well as signallers, controllers from Network Rail and the train operating companies are also being based at ROCs. The purpose of 'control', as it is known, is to provide a strategic overview of train running, anticipate problems and resolve them. This requires controllers to variously communicate with signallers, train crew depots, stations, infrastructure maintainers, the emergency services and the media, among others. There are obvious benefits from Network Rail controllers being co-located with train operating company controllers, and in close proximity to signallers. The control of overhead electrification equipment used by electric trains is also likely to be based at ROCs.

LEFT The new Manchester Rail Operating Centre, opened in July 2014, whose area of responsibility over the coming years will progressively expand to cover the North West of England. The line between Huyton and Roby, near Liverpool, was the first section of railway to come under the control of the new centre. *Author*

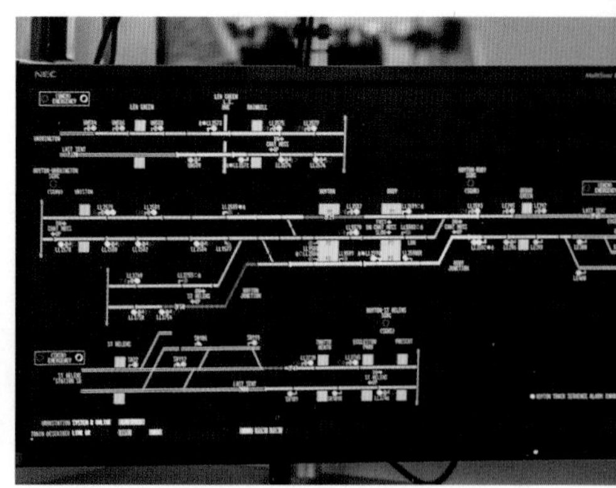

ABOVE LEFT The workstation covering the Huyton/Roby area in the Manchester Rail Operating Centre, showing the visual display screens used nowadays. *Author*

ABOVE RIGHT Detail of the track layout in the Huyton Junction area, shown on one of the display screens in the new Manchester Rail Operating Centre. The solid white lines on the grey lines are routes that have been set by the signaller; the solid red lines show the location of trains. *Author*

LEFT The compact solid state interlocking cabinets for the Huyton/Roby area under the operating floor at the Manchester Rail Operating Centre. It may be seen that there is plenty of room for expansion. *Author*

Together with ROCs, Network Rail intends to introduce a traffic management system (TMS) to automate many control functions and to bring together existing, but separate, information systems. A TMS is intended to compare the train timetable with the actual running of trains so that it can intervene to resolve conflicts and perturbed running before they develop. It will also look at rolling stock utilisation and train crew scheduling and advise drivers of appropriate speeds (through the *Driver Advisory System*) to reduce delays at junctions. It will include 100% automation of route setting, leaving the signaller's role to be more one of monitoring the overall system and only intervening by exception if there is an alert. There are still unresolved matters relating to telephone calls from *user worked crossings*, the handling of incidents, and the management of *possessions*, all of which can provide significant workload for signallers.

In mechanically signalled areas using absolute block, new forms of signalling equipment have been developed, known as *modular signalling*, as a relatively low-cost replacement. This is designed to offer cost savings over conventional signalling and is based around the use of standard equipment controlling specific geographical lineside features such as a pair of two-aspect block signals (distant and stop) in each direction. Modular signalling is therefore based around 'islands' of control, with plain line sections of railway between block signals, crossovers, level crossings, etc, not being required to be supervised by the central interlocking. Such equipment can be tested at the factory before being installed on site, simplifying installation and subsequent testing.

Train detection, where it is required, is by the use of axle counters, and the trackside equipment, while

LEFT The East Midlands Control Centre at Derby, which is progressively taking over the areas signalled by the power signal boxes at Trent, Leicester, Derby and part of West Hampstead. It is also taking over routes in the East Midlands signalled using absolute block. *Author*

BELOW LEFT The Mansfield and Netherfield workstations on the operating floor of the East Midlands Control Centre. *Author*

using conventional point operating equipment, uses plug couplers on the connecting cables to simplify installation. The signals themselves use *light emitting diode* (LED) technology with a single aperture able to display all three aspects. The signal heads are supported by lightweight structures, which again can be connected to the signalling system using plug couplers, making installation far simpler than with conventional colour light signals. Finally, the trackside equipment is housed in buildings of simplified, and therefore cheaper design.

The move to ROCs has also required the development of a new form of level crossing control to relieve signallers of the need to check that once the barriers at a *manually controlled barrier crossing* have been lowered, the crossing is unobstructed, with nothing trapped between the barriers. Without this form of level crossing control, there could simply be too many level crossings requiring signaller intervention in the area covered by the ROC.

The new form of control is 'manually controlled barrier crossing with *obstacle detection*' (MCB-OD). The barriers are lowered automatically by the approach of a train, following which a radar system, supplemented by a complementary obstacle detector system, scans the crossing to check that nothing is trapped within the barriers. Only then will the relevant signal on the approach to the crossing be permitted by the signalling system to show a *proceed aspect*. The barriers rise automatically following the passage of the train and, usually, no action by the signaller is required. To all intents and purposes, this is equivalent to an automatic full barrier level crossing. These crossings are described in more detail in Chapter 30.

In summary, therefore, the concentration of signalling control in 12 ROCs requires the following:

1. The recontrol of existing relay equipment and solid state interlockings to new VDU-based computer interfaces in an ROC
2. Modular signalling as a relatively low-cost replacement of absolute block signalling
3. Manually controlled barrier level crossings with obstacle detection, which do not need the intervention of signallers to operate

In the background, and complementary to the above developments, lies the planned implementation of ERTMS. This is already in use on the Cambrian lines from Shrewsbury to Aberystwyth and Pwllheli, where it was installed as a pilot scheme, and Network Rail has learned many lessons. It has now set up a test track on the Hertford loop to review different manufacturers' systems, and a Class 313 electric multiple unit has been specially fitted with the trainborne equipment. It is also to be used to test the ERTMS equipment fitted to the new Class 700 trains that will operate on the Thameslink route across London. A key objective of the tests is to confirm that the trainborne equipment and radio will work seamlessly with the trackside equipment.

Following the successful outcome of the tests, it is intended to first fit the Great Western Main Line with ERTMS from London Paddington to Heathrow, then Bristol, using the existing interlockings. At first the lineside signals will remain, as all the rolling stock running on the route must be fitted with ERTMS equipment before they can be removed. Around the same time, it is also intended to fit ERTMS to the central section of the Thameslink route, in conjunction with *automatic train operation*, in order to achieve the required throughput of trains.

It will be seen from the above that there are many exciting developments that should come to fruition in the near future. These should reduce ongoing costs and make the railway much more efficient by increasing line capacity. These developments can be summarised as:

1. The concentration of signalling control in 12 ROCs
2. The development of Traffic Management, freeing up signallers to perform a more supervisory role, with the signalling system operating automatically most of the time
3. The installation of ERTMS on increasing numbers of lines. This will also result in increasing amounts of signalling equipment being installed on trains as well as at the trackside.

In some quarters this has been referred to as the 'digital railway'. Only time will tell whether this is like the quest for the 'holy grail' and will actually be fulfilled. Pockets of mechanical signalling using absolute block are likely to remain for many years yet.

BELOW The new order at Wrawby Junction, following the commissioning of new signalling controlled from the York Rail Operating Centre at the end of 2015. The 12.26 service from Cleethorpes to Manchester Airport on 2 February 2016, formed of two Class 170 units, approaches and is signalled towards the Scunthorpe line. The LED signals are based on a new lightweight design. *Author*

PART 2

CHAPTER 4

The absolute block system of signalling

The absolute block system is the traditional method of signalling trains; it was developed during the 19th century and refined during the first half of the 20th century. Many of the principles that underpin it form the foundation of more modern signalling, and it is now largely superseded on main lines by the track circuit block system. However, there are still many mechanical signal boxes on a few main lines and on some secondary lines, but the number of these is set to decline rapidly over the coming years.

The absolute block system can be summed up in the principle, set out in the regulations for many, many years, that 'not more than one train shall be in a block section at the same time'.

So what is a block section? It is that piece of line between the last signal passed by a train at one signal box and the first stop signal at the next signal box. The last signal passed by a train at a signal box controls the entrance to the next block section and is known as a *section signal* (or sometimes as the most advanced starting signal). The first stop signal at a signal box is the home signal. The section of line between the home signal and the section signal is known as *station limits*. Station limits separate the block sections from each other, and within them there may be additional stop signals to protect junctions, level crossings and platforms and to facilitate local movements.

In order to send train signalling messages from one signal box to the next, single-stroke bells are used with the messages being described by the number and pattern of beats on the bells (known as *block bells*). Instruments, known as *block instruments*, are provided in each signal box for each section. Each instrument communicates with the corresponding instrument in the next signal box. The signaller in the signal box at the exit from the section uses the block instrument to control, and indicate, the entry of trains to, and exit from, the next section. The switch (known as a *commutator*) on the instrument can be moved to one of three positions – 'normal' (line blocked), 'line clear', and 'train on line'. When there is no train in the area the line is considered to be blocked, which might be considered a misnomer. What it means is that the line is not at that moment being used by a train, therefore it is temporarily out of use and must not be considered to be clear until the signaller says that it is. It is also a means of compelling the signaller at the signal box at the entrance to the section to ask for permission to send a train

LEFT The former North Staffordshire Railway (NSR) signal box at Tutbury on the line from Derby to Stoke-on-Trent. A good example of a small wayside signal box, it dates from 1872 and is the sole remaining NSR signal box in service with Network Rail. It controls the adjacent manually controlled barrier level crossing. *Author*

RIGHT The operating floor of Tutbury signal box showing a wealth of features. The lever frame has four levers to work the distant and stop signals in each direction (yellow and red levers respectively; the yellow levers are cut short as the distant signals they operate are operated by electric motor); the fifth lever (No 8), when pulled over, releases the signals once the level crossing barriers are proved down. The middle two white-painted levers are spares. Also to be seen is the signal box diagram and block shelf, the latter supporting two British Railways standard block instruments working to the adjacent signal boxes, Egginton and Scropton. *Author*

through the section. At some signal boxes there are older block instruments of different types, some of which date back to the old pre-1923 companies.

If we consider the three signal boxes 'A', 'B' and 'C' shown in the accompanying diagram below, with a direction of travel from 'A' to 'C', the method of passing a train along the line is as follows.

When the signaller at box 'A' wishes to arrange for a train to proceed from 'A' to 'B', 'A' will call the attention of the signaller at box 'B' by sending one beat on the bell. 'B' responds with one beat. 'A" then sends the appropriate bell signal (is *line clear…*?) for the type of train (e.g. four beats for a Class 1 train). If 'B' is satisfied that there is no train in the section 'A'-'B' and that the block indicator for that section is in the 'normal' position (line blocked), 'B' will accept the train by repeating the four beats bell signal and turning the commutator on the block instrument at 'B' to 'line clear'. The indicator in the corresponding block instrument in box 'A' will also move to 'line clear' as confirmation to the signaller at 'A' that the section signal at 'A' can now be cleared for the train to proceed into the section. In most signal boxes there is an electrical lock on the section signal that prevents the signal from being cleared until the

BELOW The layout of three signal boxes 'A' to 'C' as described in the text above.

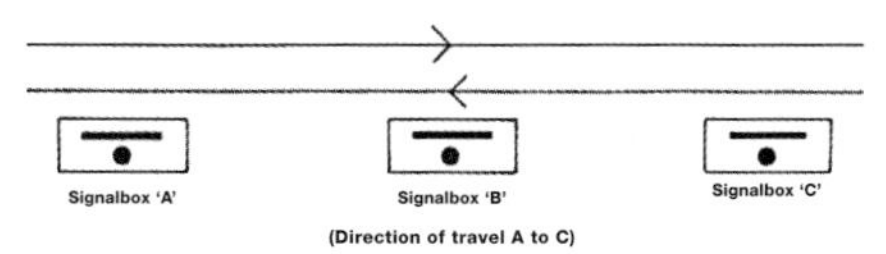

ABOVE Shrewsbury Severn Bridge Junction dating from 1903 is the largest remaining operational mechanical signal box on Network Rail. *Author*

block indicator shows 'line clear'. Furthermore, as an additional precaution, electrical controls are in place to ensure that the signal can only be cleared once for each 'line clear'.

When the train passes 'A', the signaller there must send the 'train entering section' signal to 'B', who must repeat it back and turn the commutator to 'train on line'. If the train is going further, 'B' must then seek *acceptance* of the train from the signaller at 'C' and, on getting acceptance, clear the signals at 'B'.

When the train passes 'B', the signaller will send the 'train entering section' signal to 'C', and when the train has passed the 'clearing point' at 'B' (normally 200 yards/180 metres past the

LEFT The mechanical locking in the signal box at Shrewsbury Severn Bridge Junction, ensuring that points and signals cannot be operated in a dangerous combination. The blue-coloured boxes are the covers of electrical circuit controllers to operate electrical equipment such as colour light signals. *Author*

home signal at 'B'), complete with tail lamp, the signaller at 'B' will call the attention of 'A' (one beat) and, having obtained it (one beat repeated back), will send the 'train out of section' signal (two beats, pause, one beat) and move the commutator to the 'normal' position (line blocked). 'A' can now offer (i.e. seek acceptance of) another train to 'B'.

To avoid the danger that might arise if a signaller was mistakenly to give the 'train out of section' signal while the train was still in section, special equipment is provided at some signal boxes that locks the block indicator at 'train on line' (regardless of the position of the commutator) until the train is proved to have passed through the section by the occupation of a track circuit, or the actuation of a *treadle*, at the home signal. A release mechanism is provided in case of equipment failure, or if a train that has been signalled forward is cancelled. Before the block indicator can be released, a small wheel has to be wound round about a hundred times, which gives the signaller time for second thoughts and allows a train still in section more time to reach the home signal and safety. This arrangement, known as the *'Welwyn' control,* has proved a very effective system since it was first introduced following an accident at Welwyn Garden City in 1935.

Every train carries either a detachable or built-in tail lamp displaying a red light at the rear of the last vehicle. This is to prove to each signaller that the train is complete, and that no part of it has been accidentally left in the previous section. Signallers must observe the tail lamp before sending the 'train out of section' signal.

Where sections are short, the signaller at 'B' may be authorised to send the 'is line clear...?' signal to 'C' as soon as the train has been accepted from 'A'. This avoids drivers seeing the signals before they have been cleared, which would cause delay.

The bell codes used to signal trains in the absolute block system are as follows:

	No of beats
Call attention	1
Is line clear for:	
Class 0 locomotive(s)	2-3
Class 1 train	4
Class 2 train	3-1
Class 3 train	1-3-1
Class 4 train	3-1-1
Class 5 train	2-2-1
Class 6 train	5
Class 7 train	4-1
Class 8 train	3-2
Class 9 passenger train	1-4
Class 9 empty coaching stock train	1-4-1

Details of the train classes are no longer defined in the signalling regulations, but generally speaking they are as follows:

0 Light engine(s)
1 Express passenger train
  Nominated postal or parcels train
  Breakdown or overhead line equipment train going to clear the line or returning therefrom (1Z99)
  Traction unit going to assist a disabled train (1Z99)
  Snowplough going to clear the line (1Z99)
2 Ordinary passenger train
  Breakdown or overhead line equipment train not going to clear the line (2Z99)
  Officer's Special train (2Z01)

RIGHT Stockport No 1 signal box is unusual in that although trains are signalled by the absolute block system, all the signals are multiple-aspect colour lights and the points are power-operated. There is also full track circuiting. From a driver's perspective therefore it looks the same as a line signalled on the track circuit block system. The signal box dates from 1884. *Author*

3 Freight train capable of running at more than 75mph (120km/h)
Parcels train
Empty *coaching stock* train (where specially authorised)
4 Freight train permitted to run at up to 75mph (120km/h)
5 Empty coaching stock train
6 Freight train permitted to run at up to 60mph (97km/h)
7 Freight train permitted to run at up to 45mph (72km/h)
8 Freight train permitted or timed to run at 35 mph (56km/h) or less
9 Passenger or empty coaching stock train (where specially authorised)

Some other bell signals are:

	No of beats
Train entering section	2
Train approaching	1-2-1
Cancelling	3-5
Train incorrectly described	5-3
Restricted acceptance	3-5-5
Line now clear for the train to approach under the normal acceptance arrangements	3-3-5
Train out of section or obstruction removed	2-1
Obstruction danger	6
Train an unusually long time in section	6-2
Stop and examine train	7
Train passed without tail lamp	9 to box ahead 4-5 to box before
Train or vehicles running away in the wrong direction	2-5-5
Train or vehicles running away in the right direction	4-5-5

The full list of bell signals can be found in Rule Book module TS1 'General Signalling Regulations', available on the RSSB website.

The 'call attention' signal (one beat) must be sent and acknowledged before any other bell signal is sent, except for the following:

	No of beats
Train entering section	2
Restricted acceptance	3-5-5
Obstruction danger	6
Police assistance urgently required	1-1-6
Signaller required on telephone	1-2
Train or vehicles running away in the wrong direction	2-5-5
Train or vehicles running away in the right direction	4-5-5

Generally speaking, bell signals are acknowledged by repetition and must not be considered as correctly understood until correctly repeated. If the 'is line clear...?' signal is not acknowledged (i.e. if the request for acceptance is refused), it must be sent again at short intervals. In railway parlance, trains are 'offered' and either accepted or refused.

CHAPTER 5

Semaphore signals – what they mean

ABOVE A recent picture of the signal gantry at the north end of Shrewsbury station, with an array of other former Western Region-pattern semaphore signals present, together with Shrewsbury Crewe Junction signal box. *Author*

BELOW The large gantry at the west end of Southampton Central station is shown here on 7 July 1977, with a Bournemouth stopping train disappearing into the distance. *Author*

Semaphore signals are of four types:

1. Distant signals
2. Stop signals
3. *Subsidiary signals*
4. Shunting signals

Distant and stop signals

Distant and stop signals are used to control normal train movements. A distant signal takes the form of a rectangular yellow arm with a 'fishtail' end and a black chevron. A stop signal has a red rectangular arm with a white vertical stripe. The backs of the signal arms are white, with a black chevron or bar.

The indications to drivers are as follows:

Distant signal

When the arm is horizontal the driver must get ready to stop at the next stop signal. When the arm is pivoted upwards or downwards through approximately 45° it means that all stop signals for the line concerned that are worked from the same signal box are clear. At night a yellow light

RIGHT Typical of the large semaphore signal gantries that used to exist was that at St Denys, junction of the lines to Eastleigh and Portsmouth, as Class 47 No 47105 passes on 9 September 1977. *Author*

BELOW A stop signal showing (1) Danger – Stop, and (2) Clear – proceed

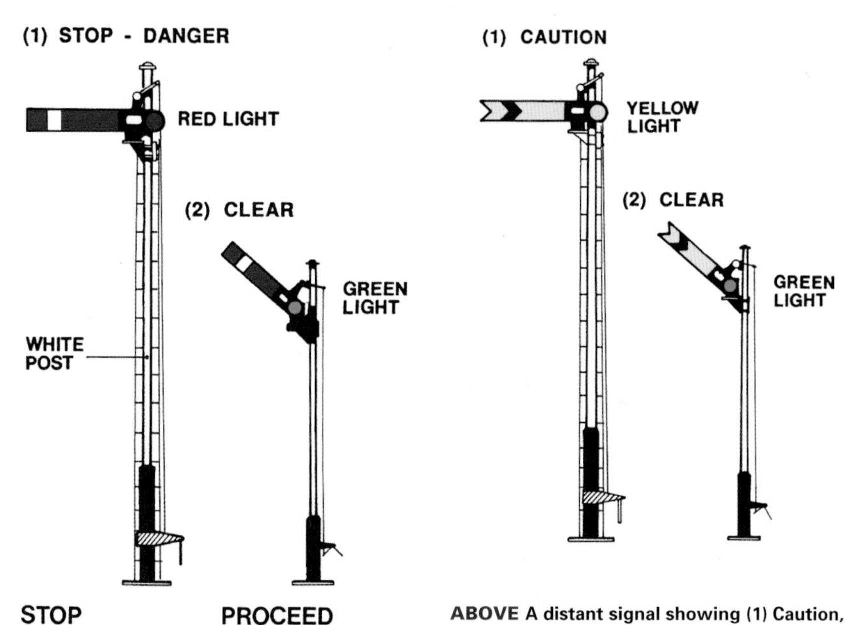

ABOVE A distant signal showing (1) Caution, and (2) Clear

gives the 'caution' indication. The clear indication is given by a green light.

Stop signal

When the arm is horizontal (red light at night) it means stop. When the arm is pivoted up or down through approximately 45° (green light at night) it means proceed.

Subsidiary signals

A subsidiary signal is placed below the main arm of a stop signal and takes the form of a small red arm (or a white arm with horizontal red stripes). Subsidiary signals are of two types – *calling on signals* and *shunt ahead signals* – distinguished by the letter 'C' or 'S'. They have no meaning when the arm is horizontal (although they may show a

LEFT The Grindleford up starting signal (section signal) is shown here on 2 May 2015 as a First TransPennine Express Class 170 diesel multiple unit passes it to enter Totley Tunnel. *Author*

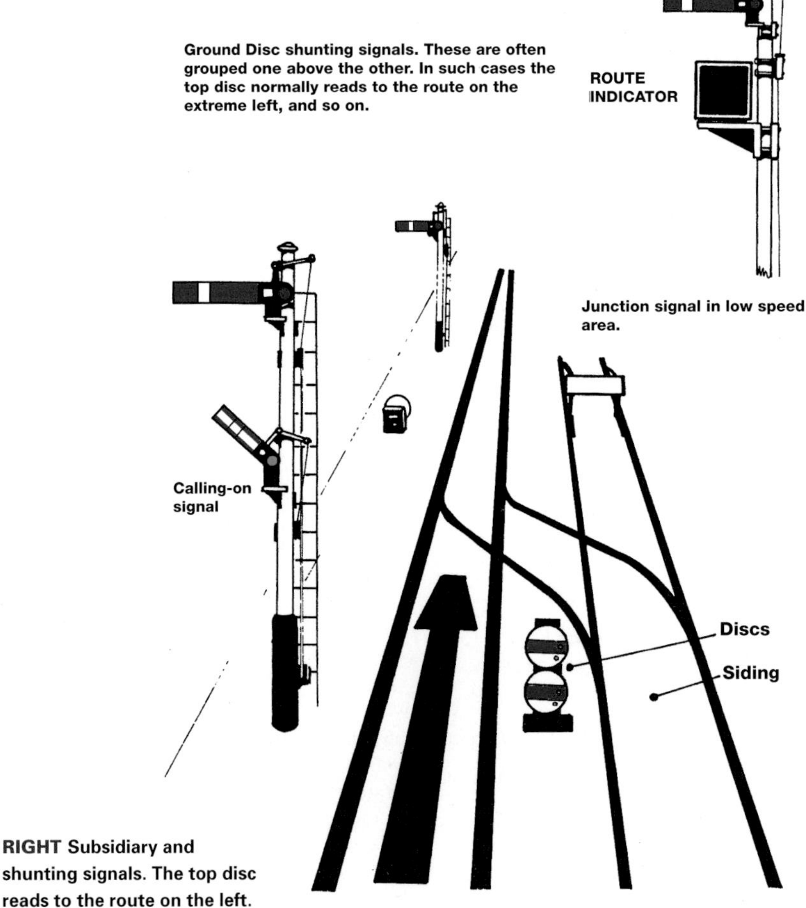

RIGHT Subsidiary and shunting signals. The top disc reads to the route on the left.

red or white light), but when the arm is pivoted up or down by approximately 45° they mean:

Calling-on signal
Proceed cautiously towards the next stop signal (or buffer stops) – there may be a train on the line ahead so be ready to stop short of it.

Shunt ahead signal
Proceed for shunting purposes only.

In each case the main stop signal arm will remain at danger.

Shunting signals
Shunting signals are usually fixed near the ground and take the form of a white disc or small arm. The disc has a red stripe, which is horizontal in the normal (stop) position. The small arm is also horizontal for stop, and a red or white light is displayed at night. The proceed indication is given by the disc being rotated or the arm being pivoted up or down through approximately 45°, with a green light at night. In this case, 'proceed' applies only as far as the line is clear.

There are a few shunting signals that have a black disc with a yellow stripe, or a yellow arm, especially where shunting movements pass to and fro over a set of points normally lying in a particular direction. The signal may be ignored in such circumstances, but if a movement is to be made over the points when they have been turned to the other direction the signal must be obeyed.

ABOVE These recently installed semaphore signals at the south end of Banbury station control turn-back movements in connection with engineering work. The Banbury area is due to be resignalled in the summer of 2016, with control passing to the West Midlands signalling control centre (one of the new Rail Operating Centres). *Author*

BELOW A former Western Region-pattern mechanically operated disc signal for shunting movements at Shrewsbury. *Author*

Junction stop signals

(geographic or otherwise)
The positioning and stepping of signals is as follows (see diagram):

Signal 1 applies to the straight route
Signal 2 applies to the diverging route to the left
Signal 3 applies to the diverging route to the right

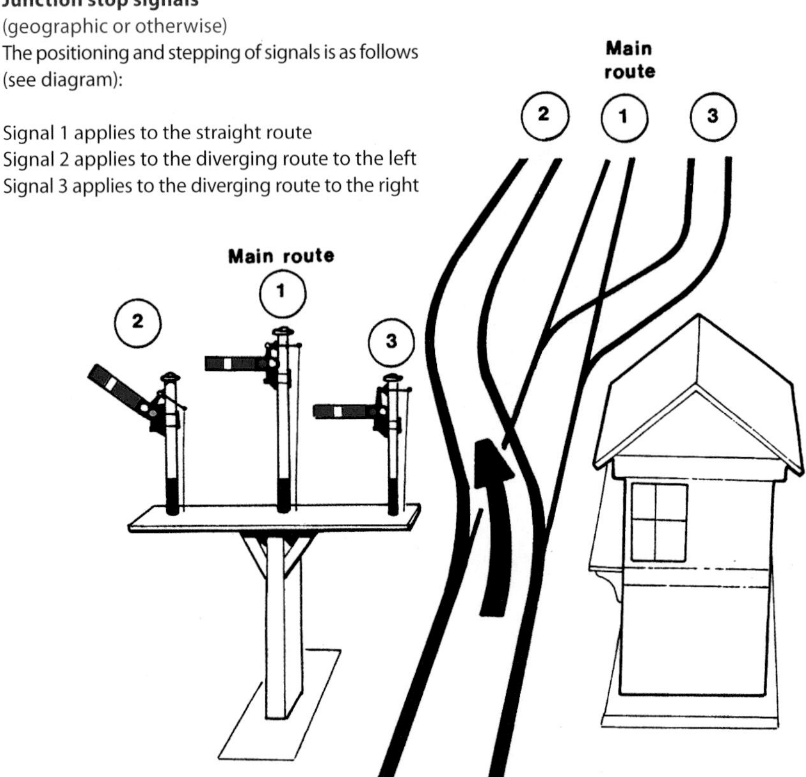

The vertical arrangement is normally used only for shunting signals.

Where speeds are low, for example in station areas, only one signal is provided in some cases, and a figure or letter near to the signal arm indicates the route.

Banner repeating signals

Banner repeating signals are provided on the approach to signals to assist the driver where the sighting of the main signal is restricted, for example by curvature of the line, or by buildings, tunnels, etc. They are identical to the two-state banner repeaters used in *colour light areas* (see Chapter 13). The banner indication is always in the same position (horizontal or turned through 45°) as the main signal arm.

TOP RIGHT Former Western Region lower-quadrant signals at Worcester Shrub Hill. The taller junction signal posts carrying the main stop and (fixed) distant signals apply to the Hereford (left) and Stourbridge lines, while the smaller arm between them applies to movements into the carriage sidings. It may be seen that the adjacent signal on a straight post has a mechanically worked route indicator. *Author*

BOTTOM RIGHT The junction signal at Mallaig Junction, Fort William, controls the junction of the lines to Mallaig (left) and Crianlarich (straight on). It may be noted that present-day Health and Safety requirements relating to safe access have not been kind to the appearance of many of the remaining semaphore signals. *Author*

CHAPTER 6

Absolute block lines – arrangement of signals and track circuits at stations and junctions; locking and controls of signals and points

The following drawings show the typical arrangement of signals at a station and a junction.

At a station

The names of the signals are as follows.

1. *Up* distant
   Cannot be cleared until 2 and 3 have been cleared
2. Up home (stop)
   Cannot be cleared if 3 is at clear. It is also the outermost stop signal
3. Up starting (stop)
   Cannot normally be cleared unless the block indicator for the section to 'Z' is at the 'line clear' position. This signal is the section signal for the section to 'Z', and may also be referred to in some circumstances as the *platform starting signal*.
4. *Down* distant
   Cannot be cleared until 5, 6 and 7 have been cleared
5. Down home No 1 (stop)
   Cannot be cleared if 6 or 7 are at clear
6. Down home No 2 (stop)
   Cannot be cleared if 7 is at clear. It may also be referred to as the platform starting signal in some circumstances.
7. Down starting (stop)
   Cannot normally be cleared unless the block indicator for the section to 'Y' is at the 'line clear' position. This signal is the section signal for the section to 'Y'.
8. Calling-on
   Allows a second train to enter the platform (e.g. for connecting purposes). The signal must not be cleared until the train has stopped or nearly stopped at it, in order to ensure that the train proceeds into the station at very low speed.
9. Shunting
   Setting back down main to up main
10. Shunting
   Setting back down main to sidings
11. Shunting
   Setting back up main to down main

BELOW Typical arrangement of signals at a station

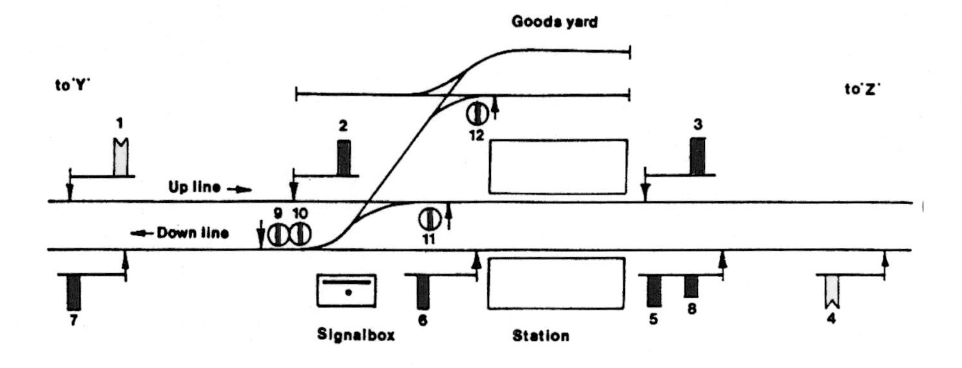

12. Shunting
 Sidings to down main

The points and signals are interlocked so that the signals cannot be cleared until the points are in the corresponding position.

At a junction

The names of the signals are as follows:

1. Up distant
   Can only be cleared for the straight route to 'Z'. This ensures that the driver reduces speed for the junction turnout if proceeding to 'Y'.
2. Up home to 'Y'
3. Up home to 'Z'
4. Up starting to 'Y' (section signal)
5. Down distant from 'Y'
6. Down outer home from 'Y'
   This is an additional signal, 440 yards (400 metres) from No 7, which allows the signaller to accept a train from 'Y' while the signals have been cleared for a train to or from 'Z'.
7. Down inner home from 'Y'
8. Down starting (section signal to 'X')
9. Down distant from 'Z'
10. Down outer home from 'Z'
    This is an additional signal, 440 yards (400 metres) from No 11, which allows the signaller to accept a train from 'Z' while the signals have been cleared for a train from 'Y'.
11. Down inner home from 'Z'
12. Up starting to 'Z' (section signal)

The *sequential locking* of signals, ensuring that signals are only operated in a certain order, and the interlocking of points and signals, are as shown under the heading 'At a station'.

The starting signals are sometimes referred to as section signals.

Train detection by track circuit or axle counter

Track circuits (or axle counters in some cases) are now provided at almost all locations. A typical arrangement, based on the station sketch (overleaf), would be as follows:

Station limits (between signals 2 and 3 on the up line, 5 and 7 on the down line) are fully track-circuited, but divided into several separate sections. The track circuits, when occupied, have the following effects:

Track circuits A and D

These are known as *berth track circuits*. They ensure that a train is safely protected when standing at the home signal, by electrically locking the block indicator at 'train on line'. This

BELOW Typical arrangement of signals at a junction

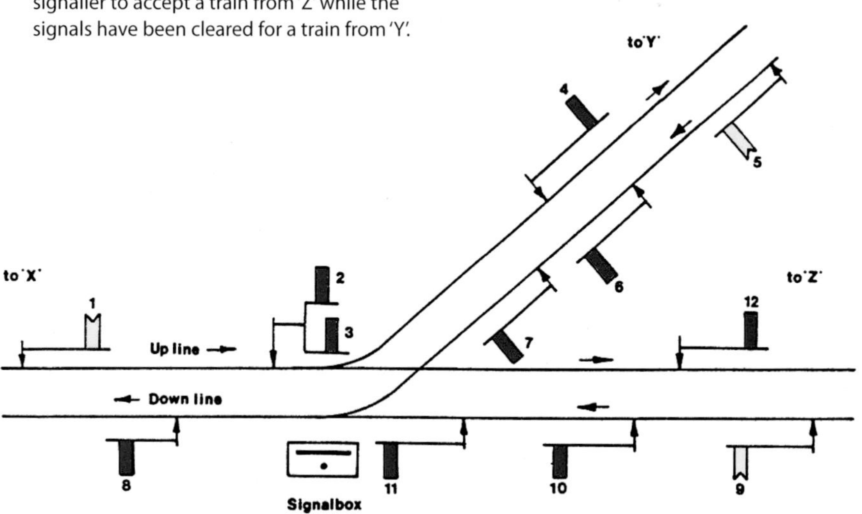

BELOW Typical arrangements of track circuits at a station

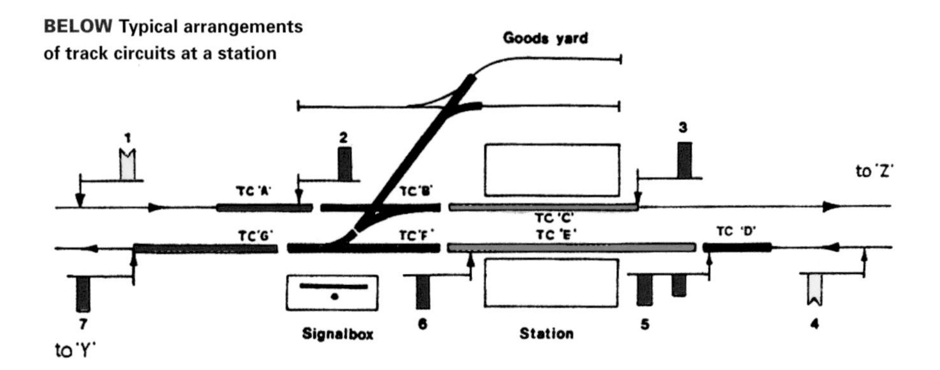

in turn ensures that the signallers at 'Y' and 'Z' cannot clear their starting signals to allow another train to approach. Furthermore, the block indicator for the rear section cannot be released until the train has occupied and cleared these track circuits; this ensures that the signaller cannot inadvertently release the block indicator for the rear section while there is still a train in it.

Track circuit B locks signal 2 at danger and locks the points

Track circuit C locks signal 2 at danger

Track circuit E locks signal 5 at danger

Track circuit F locks signal 6 at danger and locks the points

Track circuit G locks signal 6 at danger

One of the main features of such track circuits is that they guard against the possibly disastrous consequences of the signaller forgetting about a train or locomotive standing within the station limits. They also prevent points from being moved under a train.

Track circuits A and D also perform another function. The block indicators for the sections to 'Y' and 'Z' electrically lock signals 2 and 5 at danger, the signals being released either when the block indicator is moved to 'line clear' or when a train occupies those track circuits. This ensures that signals 2 and 5 cannot be cleared until the train is slowing down ready to stop at the signal, unless 'Y' or 'Z' has already accepted it. Without such an arrangement a driver might see the home signal at clear some distance away and overlook the starting signal at danger, causing the train to enter the section ahead without the train having been accepted by the signaller.

It can be seen that berth track circuits A and D perform several vital safety functions, but there is yet another. If a train should occupy a *berth track circuit* when, owing to some misunderstanding between the signallers, it has been allowed to enter the previous section without the block instrument having been placed at 'train on line', the block instrument would immediately move to 'train on line' as a safety measure. When a train first occupies a berth track circuit, a buzzer (known as an *annunciator*) will sound if the home signal is at danger, to draw the signaller's attention to the fact and convey the information that the signal may now be cleared if conditions ahead allow (and always provided that the signaller is satisfied that the speed of the train has been suitably reduced).

Other safety controls

Three other safety controls should be mentioned:

1. *Sequential locking*
2. *Home normal control*
3. *Distant arm proving*

Sequential locking

The signal levers are interlocked and must be pulled *off* (i.e. cleared) in a predetermined order. Referring to the station sketch the order would be:

Up line
1. Home signal (No 2)
2. Starting signal (No 3)
3. Distant signal (No 1)

Down line
1. Home No 1 signal (No 5)
2. Home No 2 signal (No 6)
3. Starting signal (No 7)
4. Distant signal (No 4)

The distant signal must be *replaced* first, but the stop signals can be replaced in any order.

Home normal control

There is electrical locking between the home signal lever and the block indicator for the previous section, which ensures that the block indicator cannot be moved to the 'line clear' position unless the home signal lever is back in the frame in the normal position, with the signal at danger. This compels the signaller to restore all signals to danger after the passage of each train.

Distant arm proving

The position of the distant signal arm (i.e. caution or clear) is indicated on an instrument in the signal box and electrically interlocked with the block indicator in such a manner that the block indicator cannot be moved to the 'line clear' position unless the distant signal arm is at caution.

Use of colour light signals in absolute block signalling

For many years it has been the practice to replace isolated semaphore distant signals with a colour light signal that can show a yellow or a green light. Colour light signals show up more clearly in the dark, and in conditions of poor visibility.

Occasionally the home signal itself may be replaced by a colour light signal, in which case it has three aspects – red, yellow and green. It shows a yellow aspect if the starting signal is at danger, and the distant signal may be modified to show two yellow lights. This arrangement only applies where certain distance criteria are met.

Finally, the starting signal may be replaced by a colour light signal, in which case it has two aspects – red and green.

The use of colour light signals in this way can be especially convenient where the sections are short, and the distant signals for one signal box can be mounted underneath the stop signals of the previous signal box, on the same post. Incidentally, in the latter case the distant and stop signal arms are mechanically *'slotted'* together (i.e. interlocked), so that the distant signal cannot show clear when the stop signal is at danger.

Safety at points

Measures must be taken to ensure that *facing points* are lying in the correct position for the safety of an approaching train (facing points are those that can change the direction of a train approaching them; for trains coming the other way, they are known as *trailing points*). This is achieved in a number of ways:

1. Interlocking between the levers operating the points and signals so that a wrong signal cannot be cleared
2. *Detection* on site between the point blades and the signal. A slotted bar runs from each point blade to a detector. When the points are fitting correctly the slots line up with another slotted bar in the wire operating the signal, which is then able to slide through the detector. This ensures that the points are fitting correctly and only the correct signal can be cleared (see drawing overleaf).
3. To guard against danger in the event of the signaller inadvertently replacing the signal to danger and moving the points as the train is about to pass over them, or is actually doing so, a track circuit is provided through the points, which, when occupied, locks the lever that locks the points.
4. The points are physically secured by a bolt or plunger that passes through a hole in a bar connecting the two point blades. The bolt is worked by a lever in the signal box, which is interlocked with the signal levers. The bolt cannot be withdrawn when the signal is at clear, nor can the signal be cleared unless the bolt is detected as being through the hole in the bar connecting the two point blades.
5. An automatic time release (known as a back lock*)* on signals protecting points.

One other piece of equipment should be mentioned – the *fouling bar*. When a train has passed through a facing point, the last vehicle

BELOW Mechanical detector at facing points

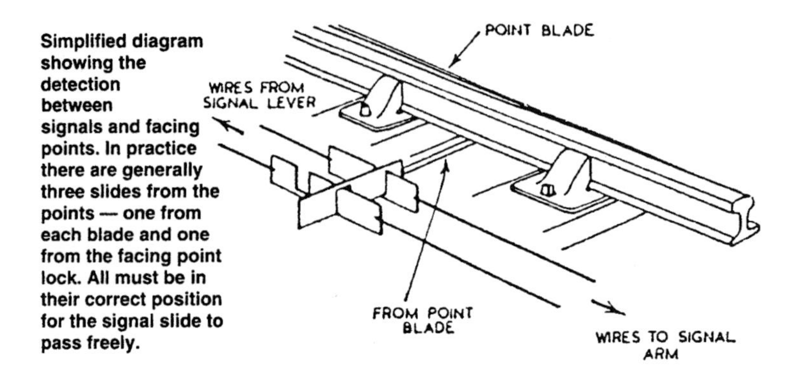

Simplified diagram showing the detection between signals and facing points. In practice there are generally three slides from the points — one from each blade and one from the facing point lock. All must be in their correct position for the signal slide to pass freely.

has to proceed sufficiently far beyond the junction before a following train can pass safely through the junction to the other route. The precise spot to which the line beyond the facing points must be clear is known as the *fouling point* and sometimes in station areas a spring-loaded bar, known as a *fouling bar* or *depression bar*, may be fixed to the inside of the rail up to the fouling point. The wheel flange of any vehicle standing on the depression bar presses it down and operates an electrical contact that locks the signals concerned. In calculating the required length of the depression bar, regard must be paid to the maximum possible overhang at the ends of vehicles and the distance between the inside wheel-sets of bogies. The same effect can be obtained by the use of track circuits.

Note: Not all the safety controls described in this chapter are provided in every signal box. Their provision depends on the number and speed of trains, importance of the line, etc.

CHAPTER 7

Absolute block lines – working of semaphore signals and the acceptance of trains

Acceptance of trains

Under the absolute block regulations in the Rule Book, the signaller may only accept a train when the following conditions are met:

1. The line is clear to the *clearing point* – 200 yards (180 metres) beyond the home signal if the distant signal is a colour light signal, and 440 yards (400 metres) if the distant signal is a semaphore. This is the safety margin, which is also known as the overlap. Its purpose is to provide some protection in the form of a safe overrun distance in the event of a driver misjudging the train's braking and passing the home signal at danger.
2. All points between the home signal and the clearing point are correctly set and locked for the safety of the approaching train.
3. No conflicting movement has been authorised that will cross or foul the line within the clearing point.
4. No other train has been accepted whose acceptance required it to occupy any portion of the line within the clearing point; in other words, once this has been 'promised' to one train, it cannot be promised to another at the same time.

In normal circumstances, after a train has been accepted, the line on which it will run must be kept clear until either the train has stopped at the home signal, or it has passed beyond any points that require to be used within the clearing point, or its journey has been cancelled.

Restricted acceptance

Nowadays this is only used where single-line working is in operation, or where engineering trains require to enter a *possession* of the line where a worksite marker board is within the clearing point.

To accept a train under the restricted acceptance arrangements the 'is line clear...?' signal must not be repeated back, but the 'restricted acceptance' signal (3-5-5) must be sent instead. The previous signaller will acknowledge this signal, after which the block indicator may be moved to 'line clear'. If, before the train enters the section, the acceptance circumstances change to permit the train to be accepted in the normal way, the bell signal 'line now clear to clearing point' (3-3-5) must be sent.

If the section signal at the signal box before cannot be cleared because it requires a 'line clear' release, which in turn cannot be given because the block indicator is held at 'train on line' by the occupation of a track circuit within the clearing point, the driver, when being cautioned about the restricted acceptance, will be authorised to pass the section signal at danger.

Where engineering work is taking place within the clearing point, a train may only be accepted under the restricted acceptance arrangements and the driver must be told why.

Working of signals at converging junctions

Signals 2 and 6 are additional, or outer, home signals to allow trains to be accepted from 'X' and 'Y' simultaneously. The signals are at clearing point distance from signals 3 and 7, which become inner home signals. The outer home signal must not be cleared for a train from 'X' when the signals have been cleared for a train from 'Y', but the train from 'X' must be held at the outer home signal 2, and vice versa.

'Train out of section' signal

The 'train out of section' signal (2-1) must be sent and the block indicator placed to the 'normal' position when the train has passed the clearing point. The signaller must ensure that there is a tail lamp on the last vehicle, as an assurance that

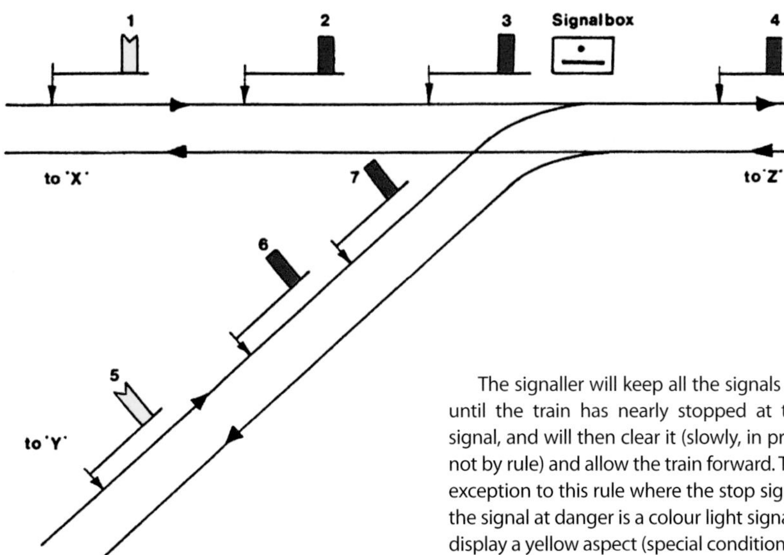

ABOVE **Working of signals at a converging junction (see text)**

no part of the train has been accidentally left in the section.

If the train is shunted or diverted clear of the main line before it passes the signal box, and the signaller does not see the tail lamp, the 'train out of section' signal must not be sent until a member of the train crew has told the signaller that the train is complete. Where such movements occur frequently, a telephone is normally provided to enable the train crew to speak to the signaller.

Working of signals when the train is not accepted by the signaller ahead

When a signaller is not able to clear the section signal for a train (because there is another train in the section ahead, or the signaller at the next box is not in a position to accept the train), the signals must be worked in a special way to reinforce the fact that the starting signal is at danger. If the driver were to miss the starting signal and wrongly proceed into the next section, a collision could result.

The signaller will keep all the signals at danger until the train has nearly stopped at the home signal, and will then clear it (slowly, in practice but not by rule) and allow the train forward. There is an exception to this rule where the stop signal before the signal at danger is a colour light signal that can display a yellow aspect (special conditions apply).

Where there is a berth track circuit (usually 200 yards/180 metres long) preceding the home signal, the signaller may use the time since the train has occupied this track circuit to help in judging whether the train has nearly stopped.

The driver should draw forward slowly past the home signal, understanding that the next stop signal ahead may be at danger.

During fog or falling snow a train must not be allowed to draw forward to a semaphore starting signal to await acceptance, in case the driver misses the signal altogether.

Replacing signals to danger or caution

The normal position of signals is danger, or caution in the case of distant signals. A distant signal must be replaced to caution as soon as the signaller can tell that the train has passed it. A stop signal must be replaced to danger as soon as the last vehicle of a train has passed it, except that where there are facing points beyond the signal the signaller must wait until the last vehicle has passed those points before replacing the signal to danger.

Once signals have been cleared for a train, the signaller must not, except in emergency, replace them to danger until the train has either passed or stopped at them (there is an exception to this at junctions when the wrong priority has been given, but the signals may only be replaced to danger if the train is sufficiently far away).

If a signal is at clear for a train to start (e.g. from a station) and the signaller requires to replace it to danger before the train does start, the signaller must make sure that the driver knows about it before the line ahead is obstructed or points are moved. This is to guard against the danger of the driver failing to check that the signal is still at clear before moving off.

After operating a lever the signaller must look to see (where possible) that the signal or points have moved correctly. If a *repeater* is provided, the signaller must check such operation by reference to the repeater, where necessary. *Wire adjusters* are provided so that the signaller can tighten or slacken the wire operating a semaphore signal to cater for variations in temperature.

The signaller must watch the track circuit indicators during the passage of trains, as far as reasonably possible.

Working of signals at diverging junctions

If a train is to be diverted from its booked route (i.e. the route shown in the working timetable, or in any supplement) at a junction over which speed must be reduced, the junction signal must not be cleared until the train is close to it and, where practicable, the signaller is satisfied that its speed has been suitably reduced (not applicable if *approach release* arrangements are in operation).

If the junction points cannot be set until the train is close to the junction signal, the signaller must only do so if it is safe, taking account of the position and speed of the train.

Working in poor visibility or snow

Instructions for working during poor visibility or snow apply when visibility (determined as near as possible from the driver's eye level) is less than 200 yards (180 metres).

In these conditions, the signaller must not allow a train to draw forward to a semaphore section signal to await acceptance from the next box, unless it will remain within view, or there is a track circuit to act as a reminder of its presence.

If the signaller becomes aware that signal lights or spectacles are becoming obscured by snow, arrangements must be made for them to be cleared. If this occurs during darkness, the signals must be treated as defective until the signaller has been told that the snow has been cleared.

CHAPTER 8

Absolute block lines – inside the signal box; equipment to help the signaller

Signal boxes are normally constructed with two storeys, the signaller being located on the upper floor for a better all-round view. The lower floor contains technical equipment.

The two main features of the interior of the signal box are the frame containing all the levers and the shelf above it (known as the block shelf) carrying all the block instruments, bells, tappers, repeaters, etc.

The arrangement of the levers reflects the practices of the company that installed the frame, but generally, before nationalisation, the levers for running signals were placed at the ends, with those for points and shunting signals in the centre. Each lever has a locking catch or handle to secure its position in the frame. Levers are referred to as being *reversed* when pulled over, and *replaced* when put back. They are painted

BELOW Even though sections of the Cotswold line between Oxford and Worcester have been redoubled, absolute block working remains in force on some sections. This view is of Moreton-in-Marsh station with the 9.21 service from London Paddington to Worcester Foregate Street formed of a Class 180 diesel unit at the platform. The former Great Western Railway signal box dating from 1883 can be seen on the left of the picture in this 13 August 2015 view. *Author*

in different colours for different functions; for example, stop signal levers are red, distant signal levers are yellow, and points levers are black. Levers that are released electrically by 'line clear' on the block indicators have a white band. If a signal is a colour light, or if a set of points is power-operated, the operating lever is cut short by 6 inches (150 mm) as a reminder to the signaller that little or no effort is needed to reverse it. Each lever is numbered and has a nameplate, which may bear the numbers of any levers that are interlocked with it.

When operating a lever, the signaller must check that the signal or points concerned have gone to the correct position, either by direct observation or by observing the appropriate indicator in the signal box.

The block shelf carries the electrically operated instruments, such as:

The block instruments

In some cases there may be one for each line and each direction. In other cases the block indicators for both directions on a pair of lines to and from the same signal box may be combined in one instrument. There are three positions for the indicators of the block instruments: 'normal' (line blocked), 'line clear', and 'train on line'. Block instruments in some parts of the country have reminder equipment attached. As well as the British Railways standard design illustrated, there are still some older types of block instrument in use, dating back to pre-Grouping days, which differ in appearance but perform the same functions.

LEFT The block shelf in Stockport No 1 signal box showing the BR-pattern block instruments in communication with the adjacent signal boxes, Stockport No 2 to the north and Edgeley Junction No 2 to the south. *Author*

RIGHT The very long block shelf and lever frame in Shrewsbury Severn Bridge Junction signal box, which requires two signallers to operate it. *Author*

LEFT The block shelf and lever frame at Malvern Wells signal box on the line from Worcester to Hereford. The box controls the single-line section to Ledbury in one direction and the double-track section to Newland East in the other. Former Great Western instruments and block bell can be seen. *RAIB*

RIGHT Part of the block shelf in Shrewsbury Severn Bridge Junction signal box showing the BR-pattern block instrument covering the block section to Abbey Foregate signal box. This consists of, from the top, a 'slave' indicator repeating the corresponding indicator at Abbey Foregate; a block indicator operated by the signaller at Shrewsbury Severn Bridge Junction; the switch for operating the block instrument; a bell for receiving messages; and a tapper key for sending messages. Also of note is the handle to override the Welwyn control immediately to the right of the block indicator. *Author*

The bells

These convey messages from the signal boxes on each side. One bell is provided for each pair of lines to and from the signal box, therefore at a junction on a four-track section with a two-track branch line there would be five bells, each one different in tone.

The tapper keys

These are for exchanging messages on the block bells with the signal boxes on each side. These keys are sometimes incorporated in the block instrument.

The *block switch*

This enables the signal box to be closed when the line is still open for trains. When the signaller wishes to close the signal box he sends the appropriate bell signal to the adjacent signal boxes (5-5-7). The signallers on either side will then move their block indicators to 'line clear'. The signaller who is closing the box then clears the signals in both directions, and sends one beat on the bell to both adjacent boxes. The signallers on either side then respond with 5-5-7, and restore the block indicators to the 'normal' position. The signaller closing the box then turns the block switch to the 'signal box closed' or 'out' position, which puts the signal boxes on each side into through communication with each other. A signaller may only 'switch out' when there are no trains in the sections concerned and the block indicators are in the 'normal' (line blocked) position. After the 'closing' bell signal has been acknowledged, the signallers at each side of the box being switched out must test their indicators and bells. The signaller switching out must be told when all is in order and must not leave duty before receiving this information.

If a signal box that has to be closed has no block switch, the signaller closing the box must send 7-5-5 to the adjacent boxes, and receive acknowledgement from them, before leaving the box.

Signal lamp repeaters

These instruments are provided for signals out of sight of the signal box. They tell the signaller whether the lamps in the signals are lit or not lit. When a lamp goes out, a buzzer sounds to alert the signaller, who will then take certain precautions regarding the movement of trains, and arrange to have the lamp attended to. On those signals that are within sight but have their backs to the signal box, a small aperture, known as a back light, is cut in the back of the signal lamp and covered with plain glass so that the signaller can tell whether the lamp is alight or not, and also whether the signal is 'on' (i.e. at danger or caution) or 'off' (i.e. clear). When the signal is pulled off, a plate swings over and obscures the back light.

Signal arm repeaters

These instruments tell the signaller whether the arms of signals out of sight are on or off. There is an intermediate position, known as 'wrong', which indicates that the signal may be halfway between on and off, often referred to by railway staff as at 'half-cock'. The signaller can use the wire adjuster to tighten or slacken the wire operating the signal to ensure that the signal is properly on or off.

Track circuit indicators

If the signal box does not have an *illuminated diagram* incorporating the track circuit

RIGHT A view of the block shelf in Tutbury signal box showing, from left, the signal lamp repeaters, then the block instruments for working to Egginton and Scropton signal boxes respectively. Under the block shelf can be seen signal arm repeaters for signals that are out of the signaller's sight, and track circuit indications. *Author*

LEFT Signal arm and light repeater instruments on the block shelf in Shrewsbury Severn Bridge signal box. These are provided where the signaller is unable to see the position of signals, or how they are lit, from the signal box. *Author*

LEFT The back of the Grindleford down starting signal showing the mechanically operated switch (in the yellow casing). This indicates to the signaller in Grindleford signal box the position of the signal. *Author*

indications, separate instruments are provided for each track circuit, which indicate whether the track circuit is occupied or clear. The normal indicator takes the form of a centrally pivoted black or red rectangle in a white circle. The rectangle is horizontal when the track circuit is occupied, and rotates to 45° when the track circuit is clear.

Sealed releases

If an item of equipment fails and has the effect of locking points so that they cannot be moved (fail-safe mode) a release is provided in the form of a push-button so that the points can be moved under emergency conditions. The release button is normally covered by paper or glass, so that it cannot be pressed without tearing the paper or breaking the glass, which proves that it has been used. Once broken, the paper seal or glass can only be replaced by a signalling technician. Sealed releases must be used with care by the signaller, as they override the normal built-in safety of the interlocking.

TPWS failure indications

TPWS stands for Train Protection and Warning System and is covered in detail in Chapter 23. Signallers must test each TPWS failure indication unit at the start of their turn of duty. If a unit fails its test, the signaller must report this to a signalling technician and treat the associated TPWS equipment as not able to cause an automatic brake application in the event of a train approaching a TPWS-fitted signal at danger too fast, or passing a signal at danger.

Other equipment in the signal box is as follows:

A large diagram showing the track layout and all the points and signals under the control of the signaller. In most signal boxes, the track circuit indications are included on the diagram by means of coloured lights, in which case the diagram is referred to as an illuminated diagram.

A clock, which must be checked and corrected between 09.00 and 10.00 each day. On some lines a time signal is sent at 09.00 from a central point by means of a special code ring on the railway internal telephone circuit.

The *train register book*, in which the signaller must record all the bell signals sent and received by time, to the nearest minute, half minutes being rounded up to the next minute. Details must be recorded of any unusual incident, or engineering work. The signaller signs on in the train register book, and signs off beneath the last entry.

Reminder appliances, which take the form of a metal collar or similar apparatus, to be slipped over a lever handle to remind the signaller not to pull over the lever in certain circumstances (and physically prevent this from being done), as in the case of failure of equipment, or an obstruction on the line. Sometimes reminder appliances are provided that are slotted over the block instrument operating handle when a train is detained at the home signal or within the clearing point.

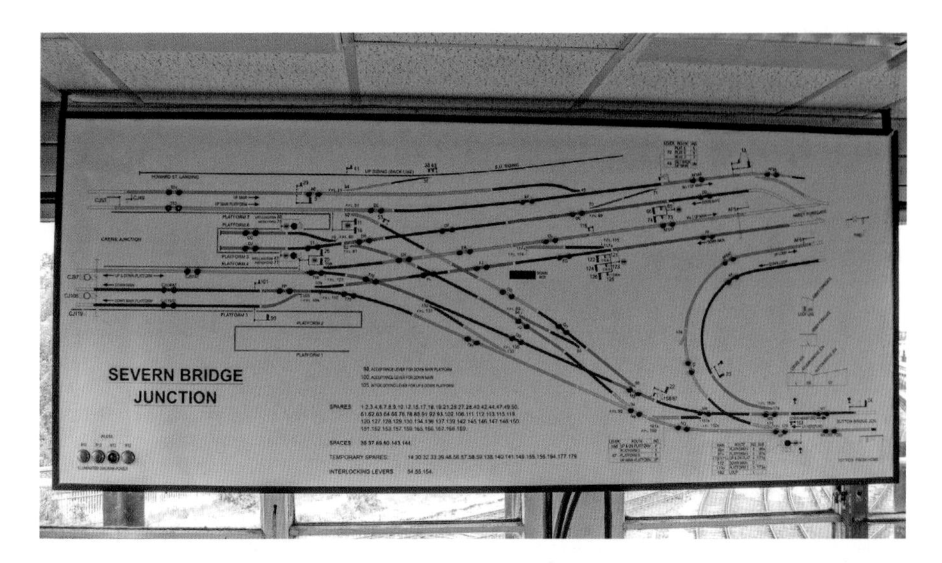

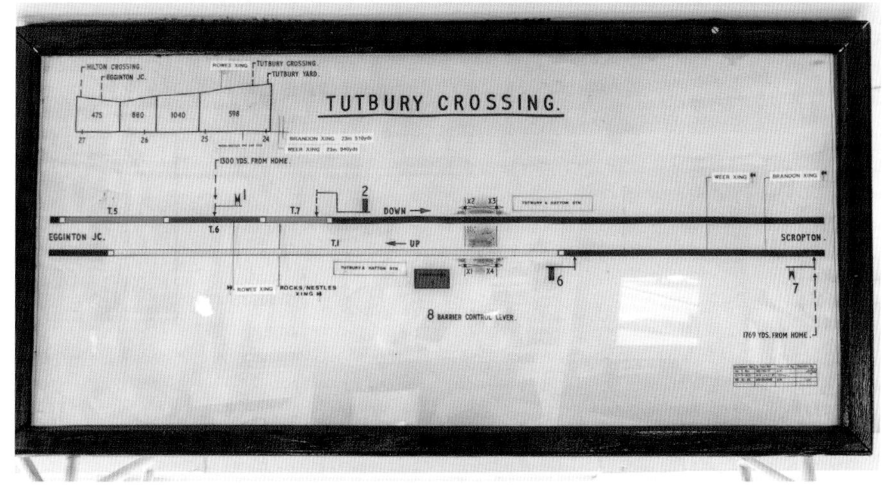

Flags and lamps, for giving messages and instructions to drivers. There are three types of flag – green, yellow and red – but each lamp is capable of showing all three colours in rotation, together with a fourth, white, light.

Telephones connected to other signal boxes, offices, etc, on the railway's own telecoms system. Signal boxes have a telephone on the BT network as well.

TOP The signal box diagram in Shrewsbury Severn Bridge Junction signal box shows the area controlled by the box. It may be noted that most of the lines are fully track-circuited, with occupation by a train shown by coloured lights on the diagram. *Author*

ABOVE The much simpler signal box diagram in Tutbury signal box. It can be seen that the functions of home and section signal are combined into a single stop signal in each direction. *Author*

CHAPTER 9

Intermediate block sections, station working, and ground frames

Intermediate block sections

Intermediate block is an economical means of dividing a block section into two separate sections, thus increasing line capacity. It is also an economical measure by abolishing a signal box that no longer has any function other than to signal trains straight along a main line. Intermediate block requires a stop signal roughly halfway between two signal boxes, together with an associated distant signal (see the accompanying diagram).

Intermediate block is usually referred to by its initials 'IB'. In the diagram, the signaller would accept trains from 'Y' in the normal way, and would clear the home and starting signals without asking for 'line clear' from 'B', provided that the line was clear to the overlap of the IB home signal. The line is track-circuited throughout from the starting signal at 'A' to the overlap of the IB home signal. When the signaller at 'A' is in a position to offer the train to 'B', this is done in the normal manner and 'A' can then clear the IB home and distant signals.

Station working

The *station working* regulations apply within station limits. Station limits extend from the first stop signal reached to the section signal worked from the same signal box. In effect, the signaller is able to make shunting movements, propelling movements and wrong-direction movements without special authority within these limits, but requires authority for such movements through or into a block section. Before occupying the clearing point with a movement that will come to a stand, or engineering work that would affect the safety of the line, or any other obstruction, the signaller at 'B' must send the '*blocking back* inside home signal' bell signal (2-4) to the signaller at 'A'. After the bell signal has been acknowledged, the signaller must move the block indicator to 'train on line'. If such a movement would occupy the line outside the home signal, i.e. in the block section before, the bell signal 'blocking back outside home signal' (3-3) is used instead. Certain conditions must be met before the signaller at 'A' may give permission for the movement to take place by acknowledging the signal. Blocking back is a safety measure, as it requires the block indicator to be moved to 'train on line', thus preventing the signaller from accepting another train in a moment of forgetfulness, when the overlap is not clear.

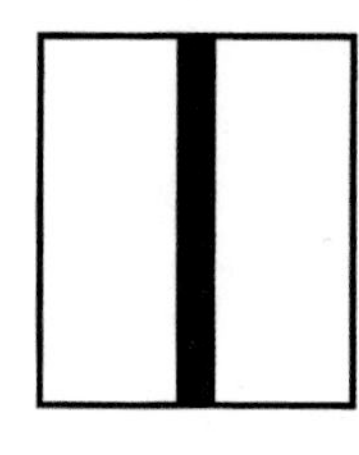

Intermediate block signal plate

BELOW Arrangement of signals and track circuits at an intermediate block section

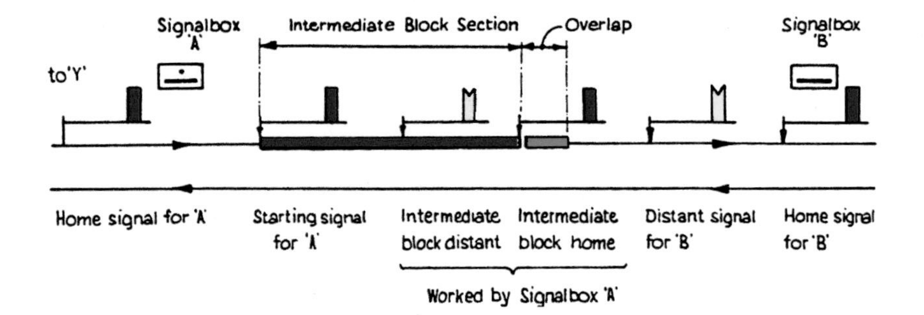

ABOVE The ground frame at the south end of Banbury station. The signaller must operate a 'release' to enable the ground frame to be operated. *Author*

Ground frames

A *ground frame* is usually an assembly of levers set in the open on a small wooden platform, with a telephone to the signal box. The levers are operated by a member of the train crew or a shunter.

Ground frames are provided to operate points in a running line that are too far distant from the signal box to be worked in the normal way by rodding. The maximum distance for working points by rodding from the signal box is 350 yards (320 metres). The points may be trailing ones, giving access to a siding, or may form a trailing crossover. They may be within station limits, or in the block section. It is rare for facing points to be operated from a ground frame, except where provided to facilitate single-line working.

The levers in the ground frame are locked so that they cannot be used unless certain conditions are fulfilled, and the usual method of operation is as follows (the person operating the points is referred to as a shunter, for convenience).

When the shunter wishes to operate the ground frame points, he telephones the signaller for permission. If the signaller is in a position to give such permission, depending on other train movements, he releases the ground frame by pulling over a lever or operating a switch, which in turn locks the protecting signal at danger. An indicator is provided at the ground frame to show whether it is locked or free, and when it shows 'free' the shunter pulls over the *king lever*, so called because when pulled over it releases the other levers in the ground frame through mechanical interlocking. The shunter is now free to carry out his shunting movements in safety.

When shunting is complete, the shunter restores the points to normal, replaces the king lever, and telephones the signaller accordingly.

At some ground frames, the whole train may be shunted into the sidings clear of the main line, and in order to ensure safety a track circuit is provided on the main line covering a distance of a maximum train length plus 100 metres (110 yards) on the approach side of the ground frame points and extending to 180 metres (200 yards) beyond the points. A stop signal may also be provided on the main line, just before the points. It is normally at clear.

The track circuit controls the release as follows:

1. For a movement from the siding to the main line, the track circuit must be clear.
2. For a setting back movement from the main line into the sidings, the track circuit must be occupied for a sufficient time to ensure that the train has come to a stand.

These are the normal arrangements at ground frames, but the arrangements may differ in detail at some individual locations, especially where they have been in use for many years.

CHAPTER 10

How emergencies are dealt with on absolute block lines

The arrangements for dealing with all types of emergencies and irregularities on absolute block lines have been developed and refined over more than a century, usually to incorporate lessons learned from accidents, and they are numerous. This chapter, which is intended as a general guide and summary, is not intended to be comprehensive and deals with the following types of emergency:

- Obstruction on the line
- Train needing to be stopped for examination, owing to a defect, etc
- Train taking an unusually long time to pass through a section
- Train passing without a tail lamp
- *Protection of the line*
- Train that has broken down in mid-section
- *Examination of the line*
- Failure of the block signalling equipment

Obstruction on the line

If the signaller at 'B' becomes aware of an obstruction on the line that might endanger a train, and the obstruction is either in the section from 'A' or within the clearing point, the signaller at 'B' must immediately (without sending 'call attention') send the 'obstruction danger' signal (six beats) to 'A', and move the block indicator to 'train on line' (if it is not already in that position). 'B' must also place or maintain the signals at danger to protect the obstruction. The 'obstruction danger' signal must also be sent if it is necessary to prevent the approach of a train from 'A' for any other exceptional cause.

The signaller must also send six beats if a train approaches that has not been accepted, or for which the 'train entering section' signal has not been received; this enables trains to be stopped while the situation is investigated and rectified.

The signaller at 'B' must then inform 'A' of the reason for sending 'obstruction danger'.

The signaller at 'A' receiving six beats must immediately take the following action:

1. Put the signals leading towards 'B' to danger if they have been cleared
2. Place or keep the block indicator for the line to 'B' at 'train on line' and keep it in that position until the line is clear and 'obstruction removed' has been sent
3. If necessary, arrange for train radio messages to be sent

If the signaller at 'A' succeeds in stopping a train that is proceeding towards the obstruction, the 'obstruction danger' signal must be acknowledged and the 'cancelling' signal (3-5) sent. If the train cannot be stopped, 'A' must at once, without acknowledging the six beats and without sending 'call attention', send the 'train running away in the right direction' signal (4-5-5). The signaller at 'B', on receiving the 4-5-5 signal, must do everything possible to stop the approaching train before it hits the obstruction, but there is often little that can be done in the time available.

Animals on the line are not considered to be a sufficient obstruction to justify sending the 'obstruction danger' signal, but if there are known to be large animals (such as cows, bulls, horses, etc) on the line, all trains must be stopped so that the drivers can be told about the situation and instructed to proceed cautiously. The train driver must be told not to exceed 15km/h (10mph) through any tunnel that may have animals in it, and the signaller must not allow more than one train to be in the tunnel at the same time.

If a driver or guard sees a cow, bull or other large animal within the boundary fence, irrespective of whether trains are in immediate danger, or if either person sees other animals on or near the track and considers that trains may be endangered, they must alert the signaller. The driver must warn the driver of any approaching train by switching on the train's hazard lights and sounding the horn. The driver must also stop the train and place a *track circuit operating clip* and three *detonators* on the other line, at least 2km (1¼miles) from the animals, except where the signaller has been contacted and has given an assurance that it is not necessary.

Train needing to be stopped for examination

A signaller is required to watch each train as it passes, to see whether everything is in order. If anything unusual is seen such as signals of alarm, goods displaced dangerously or falling off, fire, a hot axle bearing, a door open, etc, the signaller must stop the train if possible. If that is not possible, the signaller must send the 'stop and examine train' signal (seven beats) to the next signaller ahead, and telephone the signaller with the reason. This action must also be taken if the signaller becomes aware that the train may have caused damage to the infrastructure. Trains going the other way must also be stopped unless the signaller is satisfied that there is no need to do so. Automatic means of detecting hot axle boxes are described in Chapter 32.

The signaller receiving seven beats must immediately stop the train concerned (by the most appropriate means), and also stop trains on any adjacent lines from passing the affected train. The signaller must then arrange for the train to be examined and dealt with as necessary. If nothing can be found, the driver of the next train through the section concerned on any line must be told about it, instructed to proceed cautiously and report at the next signal box.

If something is found that cannot be dealt with there and then, the train may be sent forward to a place where it can be dealt with. The train is signalled in the usual way, but the arrangements must be agreed with the signaller at each box that it will pass, before it is signalled into each section. While being worked forward in this manner, the train must not be passed by another train running on an adjacent line unless it has been established that this can be done safely.

If a signaller sees a door open on a passenger train but there is no report of anyone having fallen from the train, the first train through the section on each line must be sent through at caution, the drivers being instructed to keep a good lookout. If, however, there is definite information that a passenger *has* fallen from the train, all trains must be detained until the line has been searched.

Train taking an unusually long time to pass through a section

If a signaller receives the 'train entering section' signal for a train, and the train then fails to appear at the appropriate time, it is obvious that something is wrong. The train may merely be proceeding more slowly than usual, but on the other hand it may have broken down or, worse still, it may have collided with an obstruction or become derailed. There are many reasons why the train may have stopped, and it is important to find out what has happened. If a signaller becomes aware that a long time has passed since a train entered a section, an attempt must be made to contact the driver to find out why. If this is not possible, the signaller must stop any other train from proceeding into the section until the driver has been appraised of the situation and instructed to proceed cautiously.

Eventually the signaller will discover what has happened, and appropriate action can then be taken.

Train passing without a tail lamp

The signaller must observe the tail lamp before the 'train out of section' signal is sent. When loose-coupled trains (i.e. trains without continuously coupled power-operated brakes) were common, they not infrequently broke in two with the rear portion coming to a stand in mid-section, and the front portion continuing forward unchecked. It was vital that the signaller became aware of this, through the absence of a tail lamp at the rear of the first portion. All trains are now continuously braked, and if one of these breaks in two the parting of the brake pipe normally causes the brakes to be applied automatically, bringing both portions to a stand, possibly in mid-section. However, in case the brakes should fail to be applied on the first portion, it is still important that the signaller looks out for the tail lamp.

If a train is seen to pass without a tail lamp, it must be stopped as soon as reasonably possible. Any train going the other way must also be stopped and the driver told what has happened and that he must proceed cautiously. The signaller at 'B', noticing the absence of a tail lamp, must send the 'train passed without tail lamp' signal (nine beats to 'C', four pause five to 'A') and maintain the block indicator at 'train on line'. The signaller at 'C' must stop the train and find out if it is complete. If it is, 'C' will then send 'train out of section' to 'B', who can then send 'train out of section' to 'A' and restore the block indicator to 'normal'. If the train is not complete, 'C' must take appropriate action to deal with the situation.

If a train passes 'B' with its tail lamp in position but unlit, no special action is necessary by the signaller at 'B' other than to send nine beats to 'C' and explain why. The signaller receiving nine beats must stop the train concerned, find out whether it is complete or not, and take appropriate action. If stopping the train would cause it to stop suddenly, it must be allowed to proceed, in which case the signaller concerned must pass forward the 'train passed without tail lamp' signal.

Protection of the line

It is appropriate here to say a few words about the actions of train crews when trains break down or have an accident in mid-section. In theory the train should be safe from any risk of another train running into the back of it, because the block signalling system should protect it, but there is always a remote risk that a signaller might make an error and allow another train to enter the section, which would be very dangerous.

An accident may, however, obstruct another line, which will not at that moment be protected by the signalling system, and train crews must take emergency action to secure what is known as 'the safety of the line'.

The driver must quickly decide whether any other line is obstructed and use the emergency call procedure to contact the signaller/operations control by radio. If the driver is unable to contact the signaller direct, emergency protection must immediately be carried out. The driver must place a track circuit operating clip on each line obstructed, then display a red flag or light and place three detonators on the line, 20 metres (approximately 20 yards) apart, 2km (1¼miles) from the obstruction.

If the driver needs assistance in carrying out emergency protection on other lines, the guard or any other competent person must be asked to assist, but if the driver is unable to carry out protection (because of injury, for example), the guard must carry out the driver's duties. The guard's first duties, therefore, are to place a track circuit operating clip on any obstructed line, then contact the driver. It is desirable that the guard remains with the train to look after the passengers' welfare, if this can be done without delaying protection.

The signaller's role when advised of a train accident is to put the signals to danger and make a general emergency broadcast by GSM-R radio.

Train that has broken down in mid-section

If a train breaks down in mid-section, emergency protection need not be carried out unless the driver is unable to contact the signaller immediately, but some protection is necessary to warn the driver of a train coming to assist that he is getting close to the broken-down train. This is known as 'assistance protection' and involves placing three detonators, 20 metres (approximately 20 yards) apart, 300 metres (approximately 300 yards) from the train, in the direction from which help is coming.

The driver must remain at the detonators, ready to conduct the driver of the assisting train, and the signaller must not allow the latter to enter the section until he knows that the driver of the failed train is in his appointed place or is proceeding to it.

On a number of occasions in the past an assisting train has collided heavily with the broken-down train, and the instructions to the driver of the assisting train in the Rule Book are now very precise. These state that during the movement towards the failed train, the driver of the assisting train must proceed at caution and keep a look-out for, and stop to pick up, the driver of the failed train. The assisting train must only enter a tunnel if the driver of the failed train has already been picked up, or it is known that the driver of the failed train is not in the tunnel and that the tunnel is clear. The driver of the assisting train must stop immediately on exploding the detonators (which may be only 300 metres from the failed train). If the driver of the assisting train has not already picked up the driver of the failed train, or that driver is not waiting at the assistance protecting point, the driver of the assisting train must stay at that location and wait for the driver of the failed train to arrive. Then, having been told the exact location of the failed train, the driver of the assisting train must proceed at caution towards it.

The guard is not involved in these arrangements; his duty is to remain with the train and look after the passengers.

So far as the signaller is concerned, the assisting driver must be told the exact location of the failed train, how it is protected, and the point from where it will be conducted by the driver of the failed train. The assisting train must not be allowed to enter the section until the signaller has sent the 'train entering section' signal and it has been acknowledged. After the failed train has been cleared from the section, the next train on that line must also be sent through cautiously.

If the failed train is cleared from the section either by being drawn back to the previous signal box, or by being hauled to the signal box ahead, there is a danger that part of it may accidentally have been left behind. To deal with that situation the block indicator must be maintained at 'train on line', and the driver of the next train that is to pass through the section on that line must be cautioned and told to pass the section signal at danger.

In this sub-section the term 'assisting train' has been used for simplicity. This includes a locomotive or any type of train that is suitable to be used to clear the section of a train that has broken down. If there is no siding accommodation at the signal box ahead, the two trains may continue forward as far as is necessary.

Examination of the line

The phrase 'examination of the line' must be interpreted in its widest sense of looking to see whether everything is safe for trains to proceed normally. The arrangements are very similar to those set out in the next chapter for track circuit block, but the signalling of the train is somewhat different. The signallers concerned must be able to speak to each other, and the 'train out of section' signal must have been received for the previous train. The driver of the examining train must be told by the signaller why the line is to be examined, and which portion of the line is affected. The train should be signalled normally if possible; otherwise the driver must be told to pass the section signal at danger, and proceed at caution.

Any class of train, including a passenger train, may be used to examine the line. If the affected portion of line is within a tunnel, no other train may be allowed to enter or pass through the tunnel while a train is being used to examine the affected portion of line. The driver must not proceed through the tunnel at more than 15km/h (10mph).

The arrangements for dealing with track circuit failures and suspected track defects are very similar to those on lines signalled by track circuit block. They are described later in Chapter 18.

Failure of the block signalling equipment

Occasionally the block signalling equipment does not work correctly, often owing to a fault in the cabling between two signal boxes. When this happens, the failure may affect the bells or the block instruments, or both. If communication, such as a radio or telephone, is available between the two signal boxes, it may be used to pass signalling messages, but if there is no direct communication trains must not be allowed to enter the affected section unless the signaller can see that the line is clear throughout.

If only the bells have failed, but the block indicators are being worked in conjunction with telephone messages, the driver of each train to pass through the affected section must be advised of the circumstances and instructed to pass the section signal at danger and proceed cautiously.

PART 3

CHAPTER 11

The track circuit block system of signalling

Introduction

Track circuit block signalling is a development of absolute block signalling in which the line is still split into blocks (or 'signal sections'). Each block is protected by a colour light signal in combination with a system of continuous train detection such as track circuits or axle counters. It forms the foundation of modern-day signalling as fitted to much of the railway network.

A signal section is defined as the line between two stop signals, which may not necessarily be controlled by the same signal box. The signal at the end of each section (which is also the entrance signal for the following section) will have an overlap, which is the distance beyond the signal up to which the line must be clear before the previous signal may show a proceed aspect.

Colour light signals are provided for all normal train movements and operate in what is known as a defined aspect sequence (explained below). Where trains are required to reverse, a signal must be provided to control the reverse movement. Normally, the signalling controls only allow one train to be authorised to enter a signal section at a time, unless permissive (calling-on) or shunt working is permitted.

The British system of signalling is based on the principles of route signalling, i.e. the driver of a train is advised by the aspects of the signals ahead whether or not he needs to brake because he is approaching a red signal. He is also advised by *junction indicators*, fitted to signals before

BELOW Train 1V50, the 09.08 CrossCountry service to Plymouth, leaves Leeds under the impressive signal gantry at the west end of Platform 12 on 27 January 2016. The three-aspect signals on the gantry are all illuminated by LEDs, which are brighter than those illuminated by filament bulbs. *Author*

ABOVE Signal L4036 stands guard at the south end of Platform 3 at Skipton as the 13.47 train to Leeds leaves from Platform 2 on 27 January 2016. The signal is a three-aspect LED colour light signal with a position light signal for shunting movements. The position light signal, which illuminates with two white lights when cleared, also has a miniature route indicator to advise the driver which route he is taking. *Author*

junctions, which direction he will be taking at a junction. Route signalling requires drivers to have a detailed knowledge of the routes over which they drive in terms of the maximum permissible speeds that they may drive to, gradients, etc.

Route signalling contrasts with the system of speed signalling used on much of the continent of Europe in which the signal aspects displayed advise the driver what speed he should be travelling at by the following signal. This leads to a more complicated arrangement of signal aspects than will be found in the UK, but drivers' route knowledge is not so critical. Speed signalling will eventually find widespread use in the UK as the European Train Control System (ETCS) is based on its principles.

The system of train detection not only controls the block signals, but also indicates the presence of or, more correctly, absence of trains in each signal section to the signaller.

Colour light signals convey their meaning to the driver in two ways: the colour of the light displayed, and the arrangement of the lights when more than one is displayed. Sometimes the meanings are amplified by illuminated indicators, or by the lights flashing on and off.

The main colour light signals (as opposed to shunting or calling-on signals) are of three types:

1. Signals that can only display two separate aspects. Some signals can only display a red or a green light; others can only display a red or a yellow light, or a yellow or a green light.
2. Signals that can display three aspects – red, yellow or green lights (but only one aspect can be displayed at one time)
3. Signals that can display four aspects – red, one yellow, two yellows, or green lights

The word 'aspect' means the light, or lights, being displayed. Signals that can display more than two different aspects are known as *multiple-aspect signals*.

A red light means danger, stop. In normal circumstances, a driver must not pass a signal dis-

ABOVE Train 1B26, the 15.02 to Blackpool North, arrives under the signal gantry at Platform 11, Leeds, on 27 January 2016. These signals are still illuminated by filament bulbs. The white diamond plate above signal L3683 (the left hand one of the pair) denotes that a driver should not use the lineside signal post telephone as there is insufficient space to do so safely. *Author*

LEFT This three-aspect LED colour light signal has an offset head to improve its sighting at the north end of Skipton station. *Author*

LEFT **The new designs of LED colour light signal are simple in form and have a hinged post to enable access to the head for maintenance, avoiding the need for a ladder to be fitted. The post is lightweight, simplifying the foundations.** *RAIB*

BELOW **Another lightweight design of LED colour light signal that is now seeing installation on the network is shown here; these are very different from the traditional form of colour light signal.** *Author*

playing a *red aspect* (there are exceptions during failures, and in emergencies, and where otherwise authorised).

One yellow light means caution, and the driver must be prepared to stop at the next signal. In other words, the driver must brake the train so that it can stop at the next signal.

Two yellow lights, one above the other, tell the driver to be prepared to find the next signal displaying one yellow light.

A green light means that the line ahead is clear at least as far as the next signal, and that the next signal will be displaying a proceed aspect, which may be either a green light, or one yellow light, or two yellow lights.

The aspects described so far are known as *main aspects*, because they control the normal running of trains, and the signals are known as *running signals*. The sequence of signals seen by a driver and culminating in a red aspect is as shown in the accompanying diagrams.

Flashing single yellow lights and flashing double yellow lights are used in conjunction with the signalling of some facing junctions and are described in Chapter 15. A *facing junction* is one that can divert an approaching train on to another route, which may be a geographical divergence or a crossover between two lines, or just another line leading off the main line into, for example, a loop line at a station or a dead-end bay platform.

Train movements other than normal direction *running movements* are known as shunting or calling-on movements and are controlled by position light (sometimes called 'subsidiary') signals.

These signals are of two types:

1. Small signals located below the main aspects

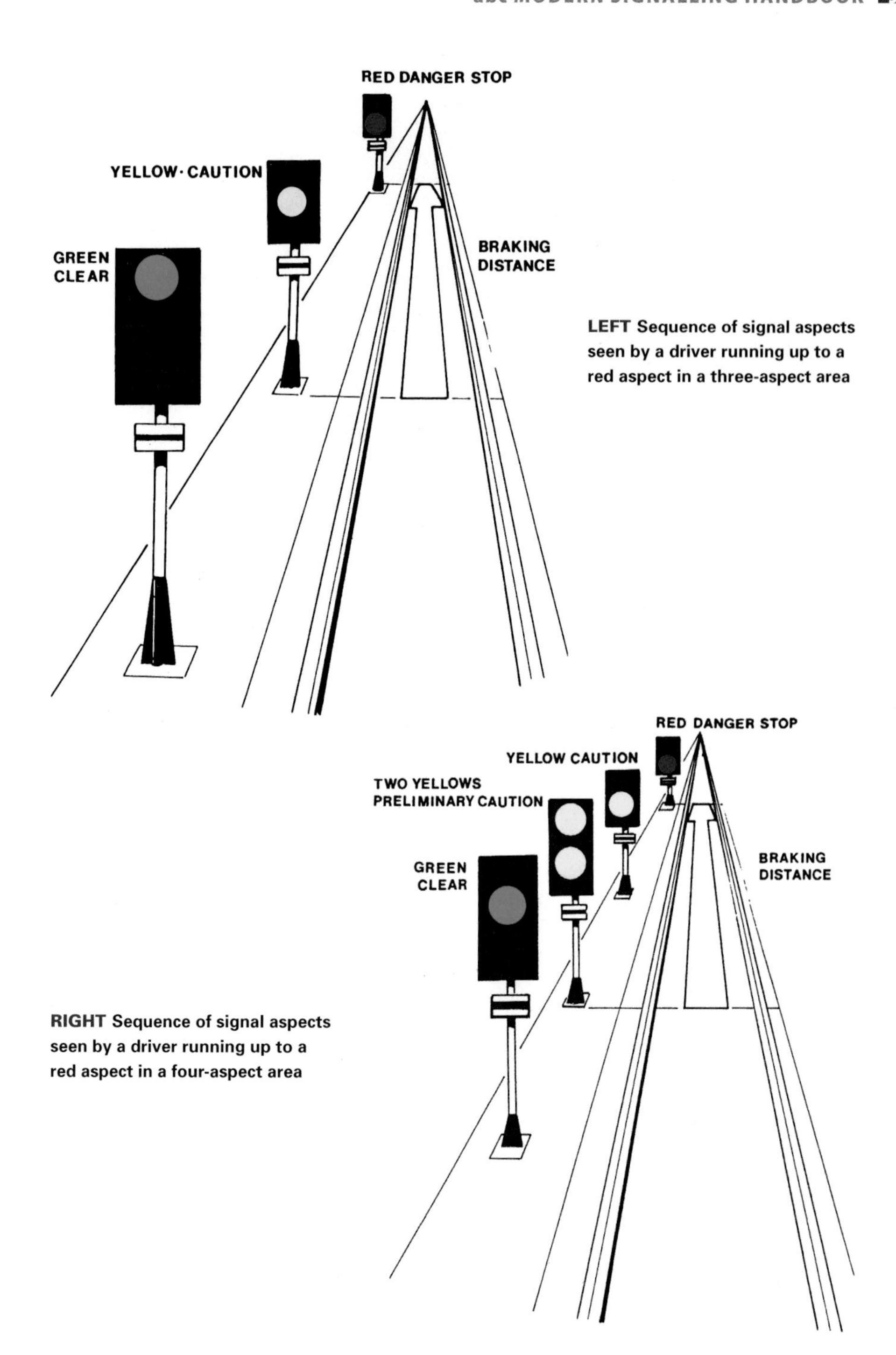

LEFT Sequence of signal aspects seen by a driver running up to a red aspect in a three-aspect area

RIGHT Sequence of signal aspects seen by a driver running up to a red aspect in a four-aspect area

LEFT A typical ground-mounted position light signal with miniature route indicators at Chester. This is shown displaying two horizontal red lights, meaning stop. When cleared, these are replaced by two white lights displayed diagonally. *Author*

RIGHT A newer design of LED position light signal with miniature route indicator. *Author*

of a running signal. They do not have a stop indication because this is given by the main aspect when necessary. They are unlit, except when required to give a proceed indication.

2. Small signals located on the ground, usually about 2 metres before facing points. The 'stop' indication is given either by one white light and one red light displayed horizontally or, more commonly, by two red lights displayed horizontally.

In each case, the proceed indication is given by two white lights at an angle of 45°, meaning that 'the line ahead may be occupied. Proceed cautiously towards the next stop signal (or buffer stops if there is no signal ahead). Be prepared to stop short of any obstruction.'

Where the *position light signal* is located on a running signal, the red main aspect will continue to be displayed when the position light signal shows proceed, and the driver may proceed past the signal, even though the main aspect is at danger.

When a main aspect shows proceed, the line ahead is guaranteed to be clear at least as far as the next main running signal. When a position light signal shows a proceed aspect, there is no such guarantee. Any facing position light shunting signals located between two main running signals will show proceed when the previous main *running signal* shows proceed.

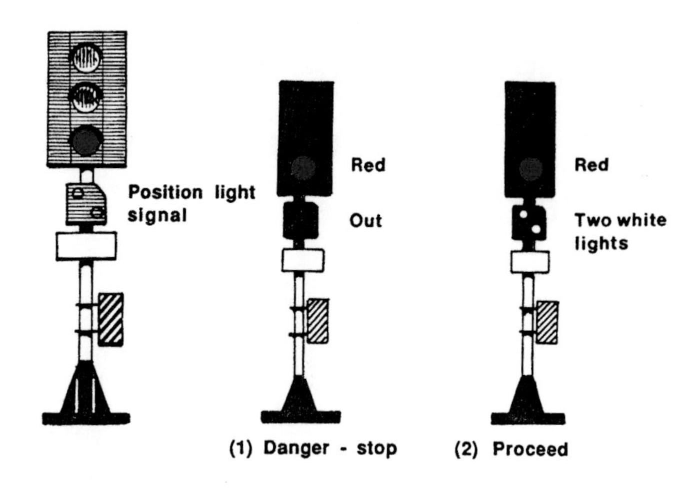

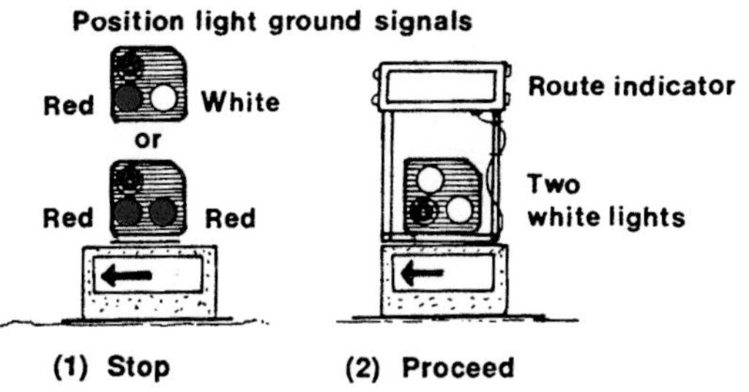

ABOVE Position light signals and position light ground signals showing (1) Stop, and (2) Proceed

BELOW The effect on the aspect of a four-aspect signal by the forward movement of a train

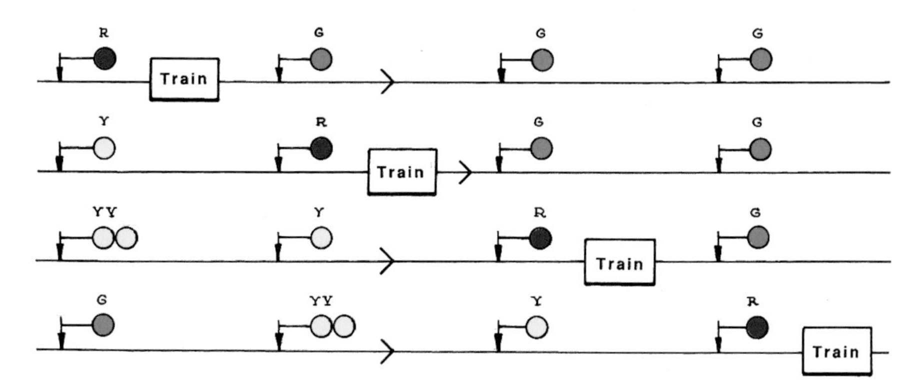

CHAPTER 12

Colour light signals – main aspects and how they are operated in track circuit block areas

Colour light signals are divided into three types, depending on the way in which their main aspects are operated:

1. *Controlled signals*, which are operated from a signal box by the signaller
2. Automatic signals, which are operated by the passage of trains, and are identified by a white plate with a horizontal black stripe, fixed to the signal post
3. Semi-automatic signals, which are operated by the passage of trains but can also be operated from a signal box or ground frame. They are identified by a white plate with a horizontal black stripe, and the word 'SEMI' above the stripe. The plate is fixed to the signal post.

In most cases, all three types of signal change to danger when the first wheelset of a train passes them and occupies the next track circuit or axle counter section (see Chapter 14). In a few cases it requires the last wheelset of a train to occupy the next track circuit or axle counter section to replace the signal to danger; this is at locations where propelling of trains may take place. In addition, the signaller can replace the signals to danger in the following ways:

1, Controlled signals – either by the signaller pulling out the 'entrance' push-button on the panel, or using the keyboard and *trackerball* where there is VDU equipment
2. Automatic signals – by the signaller pulling an emergency replacement button on the panel, adjacent to the signal concerned, or by using the trackerball where there is VDU equipment. In the past it was not the policy to provide emergency replacement buttons for all automatic signals, but this has changed and all automatic signals in new works are to be provided with *emergency replacement switches*.
3. Semi-automatic signals – by the operation of the ground frame release
4. In modern signalling control centres the signaller can press an 'all signals on' button, which will restore all signals within a given area to red.

Signals can also be changed to a red aspect (or be held at red) in several ways without the action of a signaller or the normal passage of a train, as follows:

1. By the operation of a switch on the signal post of those automatic signals that cannot be changed to a red aspect by the signaller, or where there is no confirmation in the signal box that the signal has actually responded correctly to the signaller's action.
2. On a track-circuited line, by the placing of a *track circuit operating clip* or a *track circuit operating device* (T-COD) on the line beyond the signal. A track circuit operating clip is a device consisting of two metal spring clips joined by a piece of wire. One clip is placed on each rail and this action causes the track circuit to be short-circuited. A T-COD is the same in principle but consists of screw-operated clamps joined by a thick piece of wire and may be used to protect staff working on the line.
3. By the presence of anything that short-circuits a track circuit, such as derailed vehicles from a train on another line.
4. On a track-circuited line, by a broken rail, provided that the rail is not continuously bonded (e.g. for traction current return purposes). A rail that is completely broken will interrupt a track circuit provided that the track circuit passes through that rail. All track circuits require both rails to operate them, and insulated joints – opposite each other, one in

RIGHT A view of the west end of Leeds station as train 1D03 the 07:05 King's Cross to Leeds service arrives on 27 January 2016. The signalling at Leeds is controlled from the Rail Operating Centre at York. *Author*

each rail – are installed at the extremities of the track circuit. These may be actual breaks in the rail, or the same effect may be achieved electrically without physical breaks. In areas of 25kV electrification, insulated joints are only in one rail, the other rail being continuous to allow for the return of the traction current, as well as the track circuit current. Where such track circuits are employed, a break in the continuous rail will not be detected.

5. By a failure of equipment (usually a faulty track circuit or axle counter). All signalling equipment is designed on the fail-safe principle. Any such failures cause signals to change to danger.

Colour light signals are changed from a red aspect to a proceed aspect as follows:

1. Controlled signals – the signaller selects the required route, and sets it either by pressing the appropriate push-buttons where there is a panel, or by using a trackerball where there are VDUs. Provided that no part of the required route has already been allocated to another train, and all the necessary points are free to move, and to be locked in the new position and detected as such, and all other conditions are satisfied, the route will be set. This fact will be confirmed in signal boxes by a row of white lights on entrance/exit (NX) panels or by a solid white bar on visual display units, representing the chosen route. The signal aspect at the start of (or entrance to) the route will change from red to a proceed aspect, being either one yellow light, two yellow lights, or a green light, depending on how far ahead the line is clear.
2. Automatic signals and semi-automatic signals acting automatically – these behave as shown in the diagrams in the previous chapter. An *automatic signal* will change to a yellow aspect as soon as the previous train has cleared the overlap – normally 180 metres (200 yards) – of the next signal ahead. When the previous train clears the overlap of the second signal ahead, the automatic signal will change to two yellow lights, known as a double yellow aspect, which in turn will change to a *green aspect* when the previous train clears the overlap of the third signal ahead.

After a controlled signal has been changed to a red aspect by the passage of a train, it will remain at red and cannot be changed by the signaller until the route ahead of the signal has been cancelled, either by the signaller pulling the entrance button on NX panels, or by operating the trackerball and associated buttons at VDU workstations. The route ahead can also be cancelled by the operation of a device known as *train operated route release* (TORR), which automatically releases (or cancels) the route as soon as the train has passed over it. However, some controlled signals can be set by the signaller to operate automatically. This is a useful device at, for example, a facing junction where most trains travel through the same leg of the junction.

CHAPTER 13

Colour light signals – choice of type, location and spacing

This chapter sets out the principles involved in determining the following issues:

1. Should signals be two-aspect, three-aspect or four-aspect?
2. Should signals be controlled or automatic?
3. Where should signals be located?

Should signals be two-aspect, three-aspect or four-aspect?

In general, the frequency of trains will determine this question. For example, on lines with trains at half-hourly intervals, two-aspect signals may suffice, with a signal every few miles capable of showing only a red or a green aspect, preceded by another signal acting as a distant signal capable of showing only a yellow or a green aspect. When a two-aspect signal is showing red, the previous signal will display a yellow aspect. When a two-aspect red/green signal shows a green aspect the previous signal will also display a green aspect. The two signals will be *braking distance* apart, so that a driver travelling at the maximum permitted speed will have time to stop safely at the danger signal after seeing the previous signal at single yellow.

Braking distance is based on the distance that a train will travel before it stops after a normal *service brake application* has been made when travelling at the maximum speed allowed on the line at the point at which the brakes are applied. The *ruling gradient* of the line is taken into account in calculating the necessary distance.

If the frequency of trains requires stop signals to be brought closer together (stop signals are those signals that can display a red aspect), the situation can arise where a stop signal would be quite close to the next yellow/green signal beyond. It is unsatisfactory for a driver to be given a green light at one signal followed almost immediately by a yellow light at the next, and it is the practice therefore to combine these two signals in one signal capable of displaying red, yellow and green aspects. These signals are known as multiple-aspect signals, and each one acts not only as a stop signal but also as a caution signal for the next signal ahead. It follows therefore that the signals must be at least at braking distance apart, but not much further than that if unnecessary delays are to be avoided. A driver will apply the brake on the approach to a signal showing a single yellow and start to reduce speed when the train passes it. However, the next signal, which was at red, may have changed to show a proceed aspect at any time after the driver has passed the yellow signal, and the driver needs to see the next signal as soon as possible, to be able to release the brakes and accelerate if it has changed to a proceed aspect in the meantime. In practice, three-aspect signals are generally about 1.6 to 2.4km apart (1 to 1½ miles), depending on the maximum speed allowed on the line concerned.

Where speeds are high and an intensive service is operated, requiring trains to follow each other at short intervals (known as close headways), a distance of up to 2.4km (1½ miles) between signals would prove too restrictive and it becomes necessary to introduce additional signals; however, braking distance cannot be reduced, so the driver needs to be told, two signals away, that the train is approaching a red signal. The first of these two signals seen by the driver acts as a preliminary caution and will display two yellow lights, then the second will display one yellow light. Since each signal needs to be able to display red, one yellow, two yellows and green aspects, the result is four-aspect signalling, with the signals about 1,100 metres (1,200 yards) apart.

The braking distance determines the minimum distance between signals in three-aspect signalling, and between the double-yellow and the red in four-aspect signalling. Standard braking distances have been established that are dependent on the type of traffic using the route. The examples shown in the accompanying table are for routes carrying all types of traffic.

STANDARD BRAKING DISTANCES	
Line speed 200km/h (125mph)	
Gradient 1 in 200 rising	1,957 metres (2,140 yards)
Line level	2,054 metres (2,246 yards)
Gradient 1 in 200 falling	2,245 metres (2,455 yards)
Line speed 160km/h (100mph)	
Gradient 1 in 200 rising	1,880 metres (2,056 yards)
Line level	2,041 metres (2,232 yards)
Gradient 1 in 200 falling	2,245 metres (2,455 yards)
Line speed 120km/h (75mph)	
Gradient 1 in 200 rising	1,164 metres (1,273 yards)
Line level	1,258 metres (1,375 yards)
Gradient 1 in 200 falling	1,382 metres (1,511 yards)
Trains capable of travelling faster than 160km/h (100mph) are equipped with enhanced braking systems.	

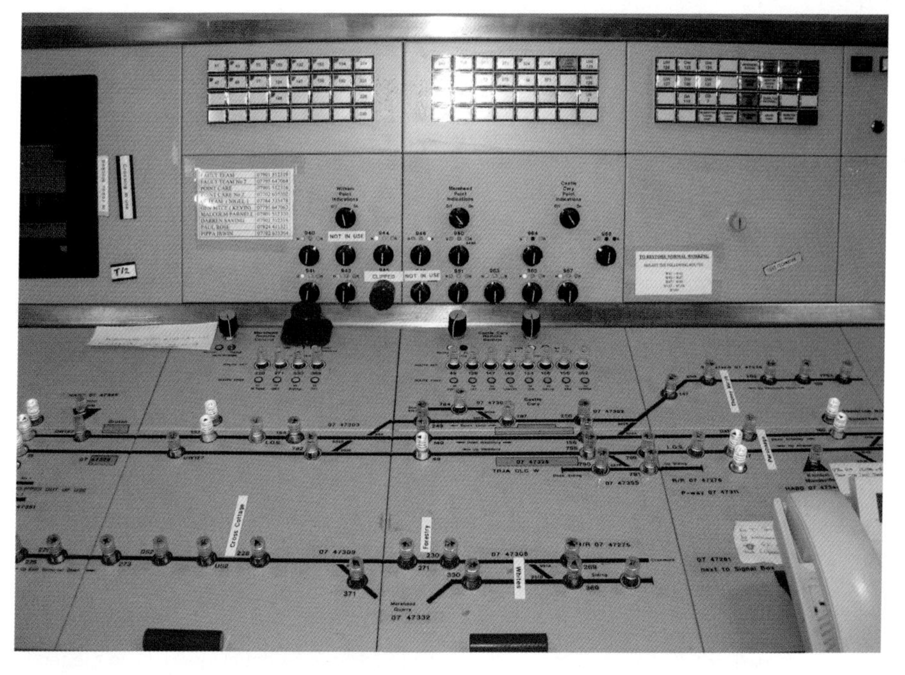

ABOVE **Detail of part of the panel in Westbury power signal box showing the Castle Cary station area and part of the Merehead Quarry branch. Of note are the buttons for setting routes on the entrance/exit (NX) principle, rotary switches for setting points individually if normal route setting is not available, and telephone concentrator panels for receiving calls from signal post telephones, level crossings, etc.** *RAIB*

ABOVE Banner repeater signals at Chester station, provided because of limited sighting of the corresponding signal ahead. *Author*

RIGHT A more modern fibre-optic banner repeater signal at Skipton, shown in the 'off' position. This has been provided because, in conjunction with the left-hand curve, the station canopy obscures the sighting of the main signal at the platform end. *Author*

Should signals be controlled or automatic?

As has already been seen, automatic signals change from red to a proceed aspect as a train travels along the track, without the intervention of the signaller, but there needs to be some method of maintaining a signal at red at a junction where the signaller may have to stop one train to give priority to another. Such signals, known as controlled signals, are also provided where they protect a non-automatic level crossing, or in certain other circumstances. Controlled signals that are capable of being switched by the signaller to work automatically continue to be known as controlled signals. This automatic facility is useful where most train movements over a junction do not require the points to be reset, for example where a lightly used branch line diverges from a busy main line, or at an infrequently used crossover between fast and slow lines.

Signals that protect points, etc, worked from a local ground frame are known as *semi-automatic signals*, as described in the last chapter. They normally work automatically but can be restored to, or maintained at, danger by the signaller when it is necessary to allow a ground frame operator to operate points in the line concerned. The term ground frame (or sometimes shunt frame) covers not only an isolated crossover but also a former manual signal box that has been retained to operate points and shunting signals in a freight yard or carriage sidings.

In all other cases, signals work automatically, and are so designated. Automatic signals reduce the signaller's workload and ensure that a proceed aspect is displayed as soon as possible.

Where should signals be located?

The positioning of signals is determined by the following considerations:

1. Signals are required where trains may need to be stopped, e.g. at junctions, and the exits from sidings and station platforms where lines converge.
2. Signals should not be located where they might cause trains to be stopped on viaducts or in tunnels, or halfway down a platform that is only a train-length long.
3. Signals should not be located where they might cause level crossings or junctions to be blocked by trains standing across them.

The location of some signals will be dictated by the juxtaposition of stations, junctions, etc; the remainder can then be spaced at conventional intervals, bearing in mind the need to provide adequate braking distances. After a signalling plan has been prepared, it is necessary to consider the practicability of erecting a signal in each planned location. This duty is undertaken by a *signal sighting committee* (see Chapter 21), which takes into account operating and technical requirements and the need to give the driver, as far as possible, a long and clear view of the signal. Where this is not possible, owing to curvature of the line and the presence of obstructions such as bridge abutments, station buildings and platform canopies, etc, it may be necessary to provide a repeater signal a short distance before the signal to which it relates. These signals are known as banner repeating signals, and a traditional example consists of an illuminated small black semaphore arm in a circular frame. When the main signal is at danger, the banner arm is horizontal; when the main signal is displaying any proceed aspect, the banner arm rotates to an angle of 45° from horizontal. In newer installations, the same effect is achieved by the use of fibre optics or light emitting diodes (LEDs).

A certain amount of compromise is inevitable in the location of many signals and it may not be practicable to erect them precisely at braking distance, but they must never be erected at a distance of less than that. The inevitable effect of all these factors is that signals may be further from junctions and points than is strictly necessary, leading to inbuilt delay in train working, or that they may have to be spaced out, leading to unnecessarily long braking distances.

CHAPTER 14

Detecting the presence of a train by track circuits or axle counters

Track circuits

In track circuit block areas most running lines are fully track-circuited or fitted with axle counters (the method of signalling is known as track circuit block, regardless of which method of train detection is actually in use). A track circuit is a train detection device (or more properly a device that detects the *absence* of a train), and it operates by the passage of a weak electric current through one or both of the running rails. Track circuits are of varying lengths, ranging from a minimum 18 metres to 1.6km (20 yards to 1 mile) or more, and each one is electrically insulated, either physically or by electrical means, from its neighbour. There is no theoretical limit to the length of axle counter sections. Both types of train detection are usually installed in short sections in junction and station areas, with longer lengths elsewhere.

In principle, the electric current is fed into the track circuit at one end. At the other end there is an electrical switching device known as a relay. When there is no train on the track circuit the electric current passes through the relay and causes it to energise. Through the operation of contacts, some of which close and others open, the signalling system 'understands' that the track circuit is 'unoccupied' by a train. When a train enters the section of line the electric current is diverted through the wheels and axles, away from the relay, which then de-energises. It has been short-circuited, and the track circuit is said to be 'occupied'.

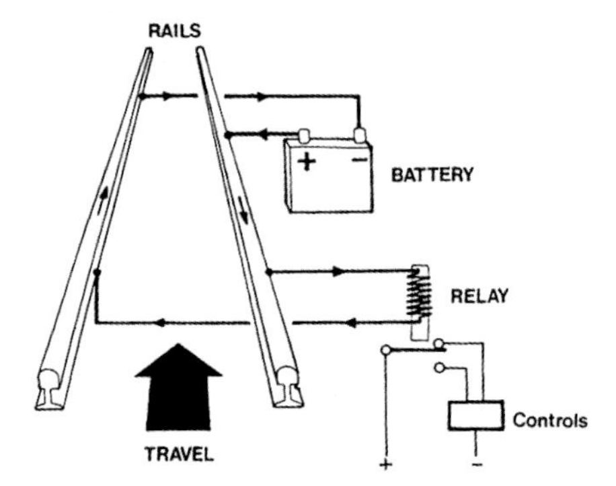

ABOVE The method of operation of a track circuit.

The track circuit or axle counter section, when occupied, performs a number of vital functions:

1. It holds the previous signal at danger
2. It locks points in the route so that they cannot move underneath a passing train
3. It releases the route behind a train as track circuits become occupied and then clear
4. It notifies the presence of a train to the signaller
5. It can change signals ahead from a danger aspect to a proceed aspect as track circuits ahead become clear and other conditions are satisfied
6. It enables the train describer in the signal box to keep in step with train movements

The track circuit has been the very heart of modern signalling, and only in recent years has the use of axle counters become much more widespread. The track circuit was originally used in absolute block areas as a safeguard against dangerous errors by signallers, who occasionally overlooked the presence of a train standing on the line near their signal box and cleared their signals, allowing a second train to approach and collide with the first. A track circuit ensured that a signaller could not clear the signals if a train was standing on the line and 'occupying' the track circuit. For the first time in the development of railway signalling it was no longer necessary for the signallers to actually see the trains – the track circuit became their eyes. Coupled with the application of power to the operation of points and signals, the track circuit allowed signal boxes to control train movements over large areas.

LEFT The Leicester and Kettering workstations in the East Midlands Control Centre at Derby. These control the area formerly controlled by Leicester power signal box. *Author*

RIGHT This VDU screen shows the Nottingham station area in the East Midlands Control Centre. A number of trains (indicated by the solid red lines) can be seen at the platforms. *Author*

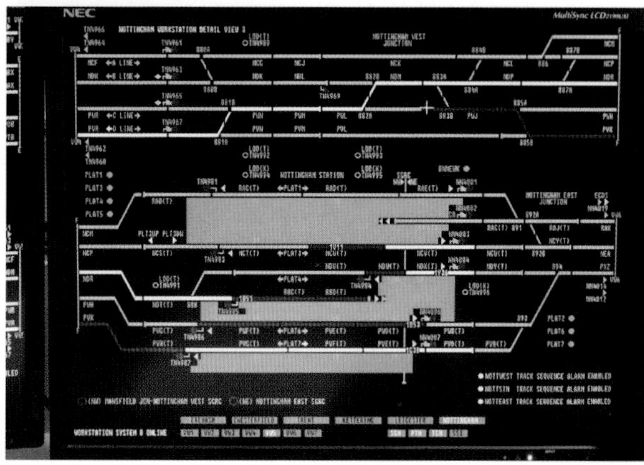

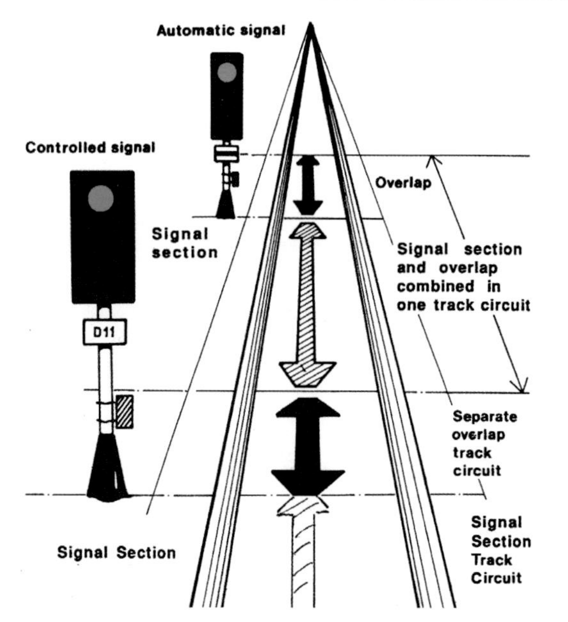

LEFT The arrangements of track circuits on the approach to and beyond a controlled signal and an automatic signal. A controlled signal will show a red aspect as soon as the first pair of wheels occupies the overlap track circuit. An automatic signal will not normally show a red aspect until the first pair of wheels occupies the track circuit beyond the overlap, because the two separate track circuits approaching and beyond the automatic signal are combined in one track circuit. This means that a train standing wholly in the overlap area beyond an automatic signal will not be protected by that signal, nor will a track circuit operating clip placed on the rails in the overlap area put the automatic signal to red.

Track circuits played an important role in the concept of the overlap. In the days of semaphore signalling, a train was allowed to approach a signal box even though another train was standing on the same line only a few yards ahead of the danger signal, and there were a number of collisions and deaths through drivers mishandling their brakes or not reacting quickly enough to the signal. In the famous words of one of the Railway Inspectorate's Inspecting Officers of Railways, the safety margin at that time was 'the thickness of the signal post', but was subsequently standardised at 440 yards (400 metres) and, as described earlier regarding absolute block signalling, is known as the 'clearing point'. This distance may be reduced to 200 yards (180 metres) where the distant signal is a colour light signal. In track circuit block areas overlaps may vary in length, but they are less than 400 metres because the sighting of colour light signals spaced at regular intervals is easier and more reliable than is the case with unevenly spaced distant signals on absolute block lines.

While the standard overlap distance in colour light areas is a minimum 180 metres (200 yards), where speeds are low reduced overlaps are allowed; at 80km/h (50mph), for example, the overlap may be reduced to 105 metres (115 yards), and at 48km/h (30mph) to 70 metres (77 yards).

In the larger through passenger stations where an overall very low speed limit applies to all train movements, very short overlaps may be allowed temporarily beyond platform starting signals, so that one train can run into a platform while another is leaving from a different platform but converging on to the same line ahead of the platform starting signal. Such a *restricted overlap* requires the previous signal to be maintained at danger until the train has approached close to it, when it is allowed to clear to a single yellow (sometimes called a *delayed yellow*). This has echoes of the restricted acceptance arrangements described in the earlier section on absolute block signalling, and is in fact referred to as a 'warning class route', as opposed to a 'main class route'.

Track circuits and axle counter sections on open lengths of line are arranged as shown in the accompanying diagram.

Track circuits and axle counter sections are used to control the signalling of trains into terminal and bay platform lines where a train may need to enter a platform line that is already partly occupied, and to prevent a train from being admitted into a platform line that is already fully occupied. To achieve this, two track circuits are provided in the platform line, and a second train is only allowed to enter the platform (under the authority of a position light signal) if the track circuit further from the buffer stops is clear. This is *permissive working* facilitated by a 'calling-on route'.

BELOW Arrangement of track circuits into bay and terminal platforms, to allow a second train or locomotive to enter safely

BOTTOM Arrangement of a short overlap at a passenger station to facilitate the use of the next platform by another train. A train may be allowed to enter Platform 2 from 'X' at the same time as a train is entering Platform 1 from 'Y' or departing from Platform 1 to 'Y'.

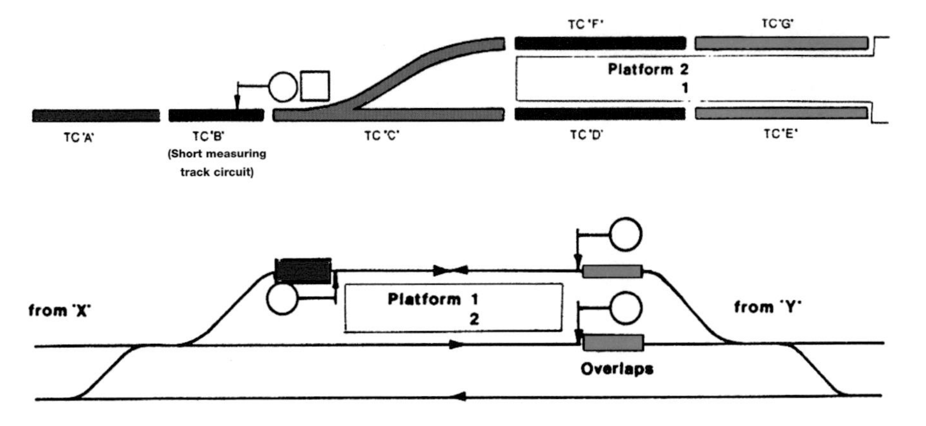

If that section is not clear, only a locomotive or short train (such as a two-coach unit) may be allowed to enter the platform line. This is controlled by having a short 'measuring' track circuit immediately before the signal (see the diagram). This arrangement is known as *Lime Street controls*.

For a train destined for Platform 1, the arrangements are as follows:

1. If sections C, D and E are clear, the signal will display a yellow aspect.
2. If section E is occupied, the signal will display a position light aspect.
3. If sections D and E are occupied, the signal will display a position light aspect only if the measuring section B is occupied and sections A and C are clear.

Axle counters

As noted earlier, track circuits have several disadvantages. They are prone to failure in wet ballast conditions, causing signals to revert to danger, and trains are delayed as a result. Rail surfaces contaminated by rust or leaf mulch may cause track circuits to fail to detect the presence of lightweight trains with few axles, although devices have been developed to deal with this problem: trains can be fitted with *track circuit assisters* (TCA) to actively shunt track circuits and, in areas where severe contamination occurs, be enhanced by the use of lineside *track circuit assister interference detectors* (TCAID). Track circuits are also susceptible to electrical interference from the traction systems fitted to trains, and in the worst case this could cause a track circuit to show clear when it is occupied, resulting in a signal showing a proceed aspect when it should be at danger. Where there is a risk of this occurring, track circuits have to be specially immunised.

Axle counters are not a new invention, and have been widely used abroad, but until recent years they were not considered sufficiently reliable to be used in Britain. However, they have now reached a sufficiently high standard of reliability and are being increasingly installed in new signalling schemes. They have also replaced track circuits in areas where the latter have caused reliability problems, for example in coastal areas and in tunnels.

Axle counters work on a very simple basis. At the start of a section of line they count the axles of a train passing over them, and a similar count is made at the end of the section. If the two counts agree, the section is assumed to be clear. They are not without their disadvantages. When they are being restored following a failure, or after engineering work, very great care must be taken to follow the laid-down procedures precisely to avoid the section registering clear when it is still occupied. Track circuit operating clips are ineffective (but the availability of train radio can render them unnecessary). Also they cannot detect obstructions on the line.

Although not their prime purpose, track circuits also provide a valuable means of detecting complete breaks in rails, which axle counters are unable to do. However, this protection is only partial on overhead electrified lines, which use one rail for track circuit purposes, the other rail being used for traction return currents. If track circuits are removed, because axle counters are used instead, track engineers must consider how to detect broken rails by other means, such as increased inspections. The use of axle counter sections allows the removal of a large number of insulated rail joints (required to separate track circuit sections); this is a big advantage, removing a potential area of weakness in the track.

CHAPTER 15

Junction signalling in areas of track circuit block signalling

The term 'junction' refers to any set of facing points in the *normal* direction of running. It covers not only a geographical junction, where the line splits in two different directions, but also a track layout where the facing points give access to a parallel running line, or to a diverging platform line at a station.

The signals that a driver sees when approaching a facing junction have additional roles to play, besides telling the driver whether the line ahead is clear or not. These additional roles are:

1. To inform the driver which way the junction is set
2. To ensure that the train reduces speed as necessary when the junction is set for a diverging route where the degree of curvature in the points and beyond demands the imposition of a speed limit; this is known as *approach control*
3. To ensure that the points cannot move when the junction signal is displaying a proceed aspect

These aims are achieved as set out below.

Informing the driver

Drivers are informed about which way a junction is set by providing a *junction indicator* in conjunction with the junction signal. Junction indicators take two forms depending on criteria such as the complexity of the junction, the approach speed, the speed of the divergence and how important it is to avoid inadvertent misrouting of a train. The forms of junction indicator are as follows:

1. A position light junction indicator (sometimes colloquially referred to as a 'feather'), normally located above the junction signal and indicating the route by displaying a line of white lights, either to the right or left. It is designed to be readable (i.e. the indications displayed can be identified and interpreted by drivers) up to a distance of 800 metres (874 yards) away, up to an approach speed of 125mph/200 km/h), so it is suitable for the highest-speed routes. No route indication is given for the highest speed route, except that where there is no obvious main route a junction indicator will be provided for all routes. Where there are routes of equal speed a junction indicator may be provided for each route. Where the track layout through the switches and crossings straight ahead appears to the driver to be a legitimate route, but actually leads to an unsignalled route, a junction indicator will be provided for all signalled routes.

   Further position light junction indicators may be fitted to the junction signal, in the appropriate position, if there is more than one junction directly ahead. However, they are not normally fitted in diametrically opposing positions on the same signal, because of the possibility of drivers misinterpreting the routing information displayed.
2. A standard alphanumeric *route indicator* (sometimes referred to as a 'theatre' indicator), located on the same post as the junction signal and capable of being read by drivers up to a distance of 250 metres (273 yards). An indication must be provided for all routes except where the highest-speed route exceeds 96km/h (60mph).

Position light junction indicators and alphanumeric indicators may be fitted to the same junction signal, with the former applying to high-speed divergences and the latter applying to divergences that require a more restrictive approach control.

There is also a third method used in a few locations in which signals giving advance warning of the diverging route, before reaching the junction signal itself, are offset to one side of the running signal (these are known as *splitting distant* signals).

RIGHT A typical colour light junction signal at Westbury, with the junction indicator illuminated for a train movement towards Trowbridge. *Author*

BELOW RIGHT The 16.52 train from Derby to Matlock departs from Derby under the gantry at the north end of the station. The route indicator displays the letter 'M', meaning that the signalled movement is routed Main line rather than to the goods lines. Such indicators tend to be provided in lower-speed station areas. *Author*

ABOVE This new design of lightweight LED junction signal is also fitted with a shunt-ahead position light signal and miniature route indicator. Also to be seen is the indication at the side of the main head repeating the main aspect; this is to assist drivers when the main aspect is viewed from close to it. *Author*

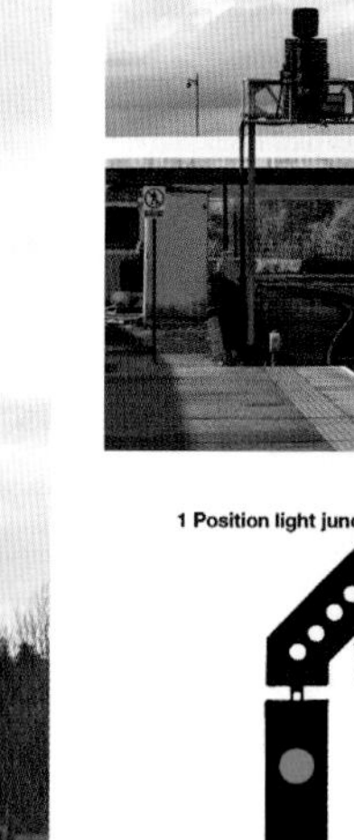

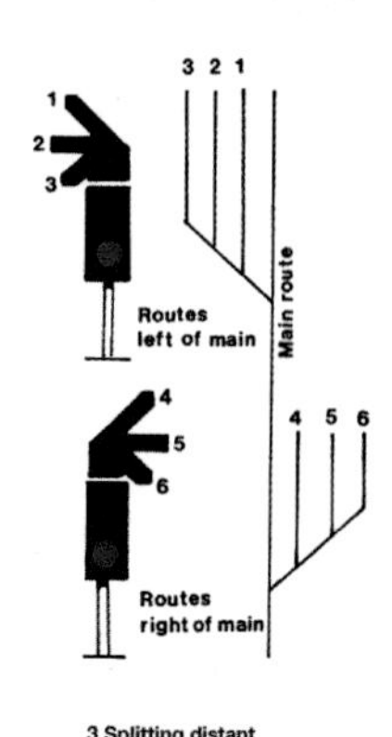

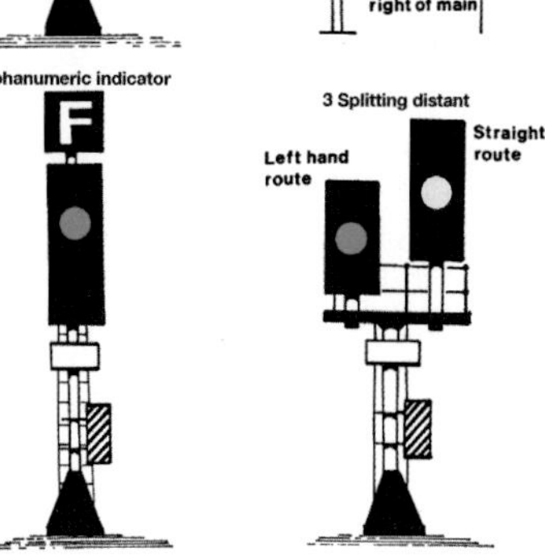

RIGHT The different types of junction indicator: (1) position light junction indicator, (2) alphanumeric route indicator – splitting distant cleared for diverging route

Ensuring that the driver reduces speed – approach control and clearance of the junction signal

Where the difference in maximum permitted speed between the main route and the turnout at the points to the diverging route is 10mph (16km/h) or lower, there are no signalling controls applied to the clearance of the junction signal. Drivers are trusted to regulate their speed through the junction using their route knowledge.

Approach control from red

This is the most restrictive method of junction signalling control in which the junction signal is held at red for a period when the points are set for the diverging route. It ensures that the driver receives caution aspects (four-aspect signalling), or a caution aspect (three-aspect signalling) at the preceding signals/signal and reduces the speed of the train so that the lower-speed divergence can be traversed safely. The driver receives no information as to the routing of the train until the junction indicator comes into view, and the driver must never assume that the junction signal will clear to a proceed aspect as the train approaches it, as it may be at red because there is a train in the section ahead.

Where the train is taking the diverging route, and the route ahead is clear, the junction signal may clear to a proceed aspect at any time after the approaching train has passed the overlap of the previous signal, subject to the following provisos:

1. The proceed aspect of the junction signal must not become visible before the driver can see the junction indicator (for example, where the junction signal is beyond an overbridge that restricts the view of the junction indicator). In such cases, the junction signal must be held at red until the junction indicator is visible, so that the driver is not misled into thinking the train is being signalled along the straight route, and is consequently travelling too fast on finally seeing the junction indicator.
2. Wherever possible, the clearance of the junction signal should take effect before the driver can see the signal.

Approach control from yellow – preceded by double yellow

A variation of approach control from red is the less common approach control from yellow, sometimes referred to as a 'free yellow'. The difference in speed between the diverging route and highest-speed route should be greater than 16km/h (10mph) but not more than 48km/h (30mph). The highest-speed route should be not more than 96km/h (60mph), and the diverging route should be close enough beyond the signal that a driver driving as if proceeding on the highest-speed route will not have to brake further to obey the divergence speed. The signal before the junction signal must be able to show a double yellow aspect. Again, the driver receives no information about the routing of the train until the junction indicator comes into view.

Approach control from yellow – preceded by flashing yellow aspects

This form of junction signalling was originally conceived to allow higher speeds through junctions to the diverging route where the approach speed is relatively high and the junction has been specially laid out to allow it. It is less restrictive than approach control from red and may also be used for low-speed junctions on medium-speed lines. While the junction signal is again controlled from yellow, as in approach control from yellow above, the driver is given routing information at the previous signal(s) that the train is taking the diverging route before he sights the junction indicator.

In three-aspect signalling, when a train is to take the diverging route the previous signal displays a flashing yellow aspect. In four-aspect signalling, the signal before that will display two flashing yellows. The junction signal itself is controlled in the same manner as described for approach control from red. Where there are successive junctions, and both are suitable for flashing yellow aspects, it may only be applied to one of the junctions.

The driver must remember not only that a single flashing yellow aspect means that the junction ahead has been set for the highest-speed diverging route, but also that it may mean preliminary caution because the next signal beyond the junction signal is at danger. In such a situation, signalling controls may be applied to inhibit the flashing aspect sequence and control the release of the junction signal from red, rather than yellow, as a means of controlling the risk of a driver passing the signal beyond the junction signal at danger.

RIGHT Sequence of aspects seen by the driver at a junction provided with flashing yellow signalling

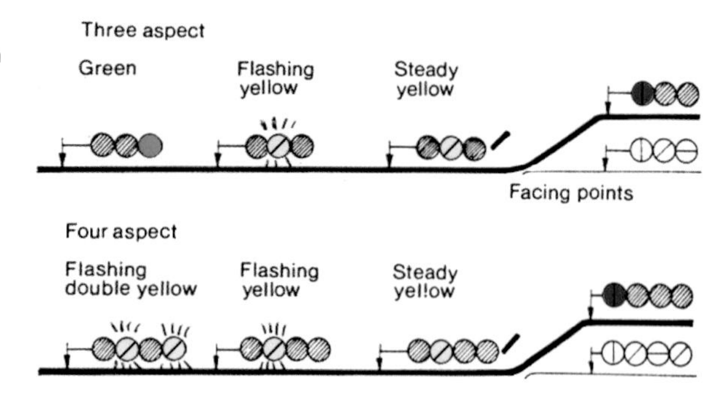

If the diverging route ahead is clear, the driver will see the following sequence of signals in four-aspect signalling:

1. Two flashing yellow aspects
2. One flashing yellow aspect
3. A steady yellow aspect at the junction signal, changing to green (depending on sighting conditions, the junction signal may already be at green when it comes within the driver's sight)

Splitting distants

At a few junctions where other forms of junction signalling are not appropriate, for example at very-high-speed junctions, or where there are successive high-speed junctions, *splitting distants* may be provided at the signal before the junction signal (an inner splitting distant) and, where necessary, at the second signal before the junction signal (an outer splitting distant). These take the form of additional green and yellow signal heads offset from the main signal heads. The junction signal itself is not approach controlled and must be fitted with a position light junction indicator.

When the junction signal clears for the diverging route, the splitting distant signal(s) will show the appropriate aspect sequence, with the main route signal(s) showing double yellow (if provided) followed by single yellow.

This form of junction signalling is the same in principle as junction signalling in absolute block areas using semaphore signals and splitting semaphore distant signals. There are no longer any examples of splitting semaphore distant signals remaining on the national network, but new installations of colour light splitting distant signals are being made.

Preliminary route indicators (PRIs)

An indicator known as a *preliminary route indicator* (PRI) may be provided to give a driver advance warning of a diverging route where otherwise an unsafe situation could occur if the signaller incorrectly routed a train, and which would be unexpected by the driver.

A PRI shows a white arrow pointing in the same direction as the junction indicator, when lit, or pointing straight ahead if the junction indicator is not lit, but the signal is showing a proceed aspect for the straight ahead route. When the junction signal is at danger, the PRI is extinguished.

The purpose of a PRI is to enable a driver to brake a train to a stand before reaching the junction signal, if the route has been set incorrectly. This could otherwise lead, for example, to an electrically hauled train being diverted onto to a non-electrified line, or a train coming to a stand across a junction causing operational problems.

PRIs may only be used where the junction signal is normally cleared as soon as the diverging route is set (so not at junctions where the junction signal is approach controlled from red).

Where required, a PRI must be positioned beyond but close to any signal before the junction signal that would show a more restrictive aspect than that for the normal junction sequence if the junction signal was at red. Where the signalling is four-aspect, the number of PRIs fitted (one or two) depends on the speed of the junction – only one is necessary at a lower-speed junction.

Splitting banner repeating signals

Where a junction signal that requires a *banner repeating signal* has one or more routes preceded by flashing aspects, splitting distants or a double yellow aspect (i.e. approach control from yellow), a splitting banner repeating signal must be provided instead of a single banner. The banner head for the diverging route must be fitted lower than that for the main route, and must only clear when the junction signal has cleared for the diverging route.

Temporary speed restriction on a diverging route

Where there is a temporary speed restriction on a diverging route, it is essential that drivers know which way the junction points are set, so that they can reduce speed as necessary for the temporary speed restriction. Therefore, where the junction is normally signalled to allow for higher speeds, a temporary approach control from red arrangement must be applied to hold the junction signal at red until the route indication is readable by the driver.

Approach locking of points

The purpose of *approach locking* is to prevent a route ahead of a signal from being changed once the driver has seen a proceed aspect at the junction signal (or a green aspect two signals away, or a double yellow aspect at the previous signal). However, provision is made for the locking to be released provided that, if the junction signal is replaced to danger, sufficient time has elapsed either for the train to have come to a stand at the junction signal, or to have run past it on to track circuits that lock the points.

Approach locking becomes operative immediately a proceed aspect has been displayed at the junction signal. It is released in the following ways:

1. When the train passes the signal
2. By the operation of a time release, which is generally between one and four minutes depending on the distance between signals, the type of traffic on the line concerned (passenger only, or mixed traffic), and the nature of the location (e.g. a major station or critical junction)
3. By a system known as 'comprehensive approach locking', which detects whether there is any train approaching a point where the driver would see a change of aspect by the replacement of a signal to red; this facilitates a quicker release of approach locking but adds to the complexity of the circuitry.

Time of operation locking of points

Time of operation locking is fitted where there are facing points within a distance of 20 metres (22 yards) beyond a stop signal, and is required to prevent a train that has inadvertently passed that signal at danger from derailing on the facing points if they could otherwise be moved by the signaller. The locking is released, with the signal remaining at red, either by the track circuit or axle counter section before the signal being detected clear, or by being detected occupied for sufficient time to indicate that a train has stopped correctly before the signal.

Other junction considerations, including flank protection

Worthy of mention are some other items regarding junctions:

1. A junction signal must not be more than 800 metres (880 yards) from the facing points to which it applies.
2. *Flank protection* may be provided at junctions to protect a train from another one

LEFT PRI warning of junction indicator in position 1 ahead

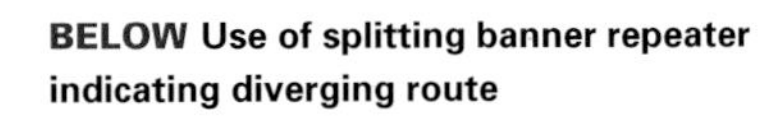

BELOW Use of splitting banner repeater indicating diverging route

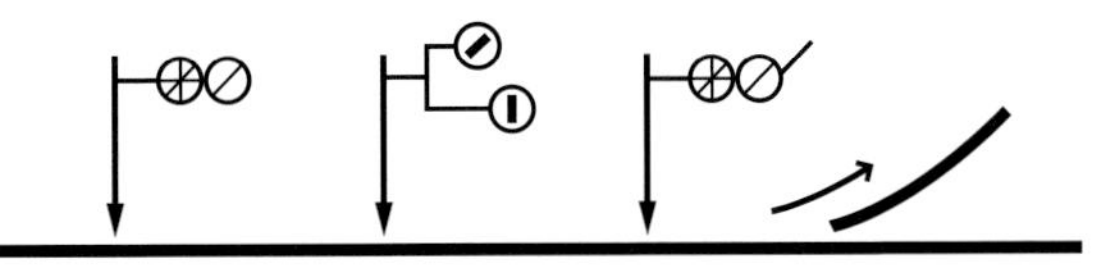

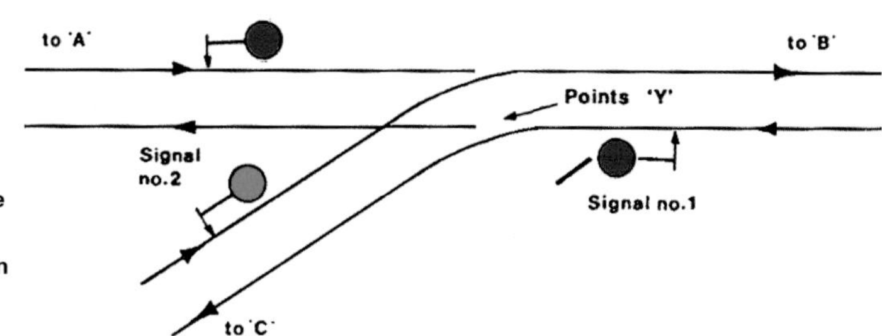

RIGHT An example of flank protection at a double junction

approaching the junction, which may have run past a signal at danger (see the accompanying diagram). Before signal 2 can be cleared, points Y must be set towards C to protect a train proceeding from C to B against another train requiring to proceed from B to A, which may wrongly have passed signal 1 at danger. In more complex layouts, it is preferable for an overrunning train to be diverted onto a line used predominantly by trains in the same direction.

3. If drivers find that a junction signal has been cleared for the wrong route, or receive *flashing yellow aspects* when they are expecting to proceed along the highest-speed route, or receive *clear signals* at signals in rear of a junction at which they are expecting to be diverted, they must stop at the junction signal if possible (and if it is safe to do so) and speak to the signaller. If preliminary route indicators are fitted (see above), they should enable drivers to stop at the junction signal.

The complexity of junction signalling arrangements

The signalling arrangements for the safe working of trains through diverging junctions where a reduction of speed is necessary have become increasingly complex. This has occurred as design speeds have increased in response to the competitive need for faster journey times and to increase line capacity. The arrangements set out in this chapter are designed to allow the intended speed of the junction to be achieved safely, and this is done through controls on the signalling so that safety is assured even if the driver should make an error. Flashing yellow aspects are sometimes provided to allow the design speed of the turnout to be achieved.

Finally, while the British system of signalling is based on drivers having a detailed knowledge of the routes over which they drive (otherwise known as 'route signalling'), junction signalling introduces elements of speed signalling more commonly found elsewhere in Europe.

CHAPTER 16

Inside a modern signalling control centre

Control by push-button panel

The large signalling control centres known as *power signal boxes*, which use route-relay interlocking, were mostly brought into use in the 1960s and 1970s and still control many main lines in Britain. Generally speaking, the technical equipment is housed on the ground floor or lower floors, while the operating room is located on the upper floor.

The most distinctive feature of the operating room is the control panel, sometimes referred to as an *NX panel*, the NX standing for entrance/exit, which usually occupies the full length of one side, or may even be horseshoe-shaped. The panel displays a geographical representation of all the lines controlled from the signal box and contains all the operating switches and buttons for use by the signallers, of whom there may be any number from two to a dozen or more. Behind the signallers are a number of desks for train regulators, supervisors, announcers and assistants, etc.

The signaller's role is to set the routes for trains, and clear the signals, in accordance with the timetable, and, when trains run late, to minimise the effect of such late running. The signallers therefore need to know about trains approaching their area of control so that they can make the most appropriate regulating decisions, and can see where all trains are by looking at the control panel.

In order to set a route and clear the signals for a train, the signaller presses the entrance button alongside the first controlled signal on the control panel. The button will then show a white flashing light. The next step is to press the exit button at the next controlled signal along the route to be taken by the approaching train (one button normally serves as both an entrance and an exit button). If the route is available (i.e. has not been 'promised' to another train), all the points are moved to their appropriate position and locked for the safety of the train. Then, if all the required track circuits in the route are clear, the first controlled signal changes to a proceed aspect. The signal indication on the control panel will show a green light irrespective of whether the lineside signal itself is showing green, one yellow or two yellows. A row of white lights is displayed on the control panel along the route concerned to confirm to the signaller that it has been successfully set. The signaller then repeats the procedure further along the route to be taken by the train until the whole of the route within the signaller's area of control has been set.

When the train enters the route concerned and occupies the first track circuit, its presence will be indicated to the signaller by a number of red lights on the line on the control panel, and as the train moves along and occupies and subsequently clears further track circuits the row of red lights on the control panel will step along accordingly, so that the signaller can always tell which track circuit is being occupied by the train. It is not normally possible to tell exactly where the train is if only one track circuit is showing occupied, but if two are showing occupied it is a fair deduction that the train is straddling the boundary between them.

As the train proceeds on its way the signals will change to danger behind it, but the row of white route lights will remain on the control panel until either the signaller cancels the route by pulling out the entrance button, or they are extinguished by the automatic operation of train-operated route release equipment, which is provided where it is reasonable to do so.

To enable the signallers to carry out their regulating duties they need to know the identity of trains. All trains in the timetable have a four-character identity number and each train displays its number on the control panel in windows or berths along the route concerned. As the train proceeds on its way and occupies track circuits in sequence, the train description displayed on the control panel steps forward from berth to berth accordingly. There is one

exception to this in older power signal boxes: if the train passes a signal at danger the track circuit indications on the control panel will step forward normally, but the train description will remain in the berth on the approach side of the signal concerned; the train description will not pass a signal at danger. This provides important evidence in cases where a signal is wrongly passed at danger and the aspect displayed by the signal is disputed by the driver.

In most power signal boxes the control panel is arranged almost vertically and combines both the controls and the indications. The signallers walk to and fro to reach the various controls on that section of the panel under their jurisdiction. In some of the larger and busier signal boxes, such as London Victoria, the controls are removed from the panel and provided on a separate console at which the signaller sits. This is more expensive but enables the signaller to have a wider overview of the panel and may lead to the improved regulation of trains in dense and complex traffic conditions.

The control panels contain other equipment besides the geographical display, such as:

1. Individual point switches, to change the position of points in abnormal circumstances

ABOVE The 'OFF' indicator is illuminated at the west end of Platform 12 at Leeds, telling station staff and the train guard that the signal at the end of the platform has been cleared for the train to depart. Station staff may now indicate to the guard that station duties have been completed and the train doors are closed. The guard may then signal to the driver that it is safe to depart. The train is 1V50, the 09.08 CrossCountry service to Plymouth on 27 January 2016. It may also be noted that as well as a green aspect, the route indicator is displaying the letter 'D', meaning that the train will be taking line 'D'; one of the six lines 'A' to 'F' at the west end of Leeds station. *Author*

2. Indicators, showing which way the points are lying. The two positions are known as *normal* and *reverse*. There is a third indication, known as *out of correspondence*, which is illuminated when the points have failed to move across correctly from one position to the other, or when they have been damaged in an accident. Signals will not clear if points are showing 'out of correspondence'.
3. Telephones, giving communication at each signal (*signal post telephones*) with drivers and anyone else who may need to speak

to the signaller, e.g. trackworkers and signal technicians. When the telephone is used, the number of the signal at which the telephone is located is displayed on a display screen to assist the signaller in identifying the origin of the call. The rules also require callers to identify themselves and say where they are calling from. Communication can often only be established from the signal to the signal box; the signaller may not be able to ring the telephone instrument at the signal.

4. Telephones, giving communication to stations, offices, etc, through the normal railway fixed telephone network
5. Radio equipment allowing communication with drivers (see Chapter 35)
6. Level crossing indications and controls
7. Hot axle box and wheel impact load warning equipment (see Chapter 32.
8. 'Train ready to start' (TRTS) indications. At larger stations, where trains may be detained for reasons not apparent to the signaller, it may be advantageous for the setting of the route to be delayed until the train is ready to depart, thus allowing the route to be used by other trains. When a train is ready to depart, the signaller is informed by railway staff operating a *train ready to start plunger* on the platform, which causes a yellow light to flash on the control panel at the end of the platform concerned
9. Releases to ground frames, shunt frames, level crossing boxes, etc
10. Emergency replacement buttons and indications, for automatic and semi-automatic signals
11. Automatic working of controlled signals. The signaller can convert a controlled signal to automatic operation by pressing an 'A' button sited next to the signal on the panel, after the route has been set. The 'A' button will then show a white light. Automatic operation can be cancelled at any time merely by pulling out the 'A' button, but doing this does not cancel the route.

Control from computer workstation

In the more recent signal boxes, IECCs and signalling control centres, the signaller's control panel has been replaced by a number of signaller's work-stations based on the use of visual display units (VDUs). VDU equipment is cheaper, and requires far less space, than conventional control panels. This has been coupled with the technical change from relay

BELOW The operating floor at the Manchester Rail Operating Centre, showing a number of signallers' workstations. These will grow in number as more and more of the railway in North West England is controlled from here. *Author*

interlocking to computer-based interlocking, which also needs much less space. The whole signal box structure can therefore be smaller in proportion to the amount of track miles controlled.

The computer workstations usually consist of four or more VDUs located on a curved desk with a trackerball and keyboard to set routes. Typically, two of the screens are used to display an overview of the signaller's control area, with a third screen being able to be used to call up a detailed view of the controlled area. The fourth screen is used for fault/failure reporting and enable the signaller to input data relating to the train describer and automatic route setting functions (described below). Typical alarms, which may include an audible alert, include a failure of the signalling control system, or a signal passed at danger (*SPAD*), this latter having been introduced in response to the serious train collision, following a SPAD, at Ladbroke Grove on 5 October 1999.

The principle of operation remains the same – in order to set a route, the signaller uses the trackerball to move the cursor on the VDU screen to the signal at the entrance to the route to be set, then enters the command by depressing a button. The next operation is to move the cursor to the exit signal of the route, and activate the setting of the route. This changes the depiction

ABOVE The Burton-on-Trent workstation in the East Midlands Control Centre. Among the various screens can be seen the monitor for Clay Mills manually controlled barrier crossing and the telephone concentrator (second from right, bottom). On the desk can be seen (from left) the train register book, the (yellow) trackerball and the panel for operating Clay Mills crossing. *Author*

of the route on the VDU from a grey line to a white line, which changes to a red line when it becomes occupied by a train. Alternatively, as a back-up, the signaller can set the route by the use of the keyboard, entering the numbers of the entrance and exit signals.

Signals on the screen are shown with a red roundel when at danger, a yellow roundel when at yellow/double yellow, and a green roundel when at green. Other information can be shown on screen by highlighting the area concerned, for example a blue background when a signaller has applied a reminder.

Other equipment provided at each workstation may include:

1. A computer terminal, which the signaller can use to access information systems such as the

Control Centre of the Future (CCF). CCF provides a visual display of train movements in real time, showing the extent of any late running (it can also be used retrospectively). The system is driven by train describers and is the key to the *delay attribution* process.
2. A telephone *concentrator* terminal through which the signaller can speak to railway staff calling in from lineside telephones, such as signal post telephones and points
3. Radio equipment through which signallers can speak to drivers (Chapter 35)
4. One or more CCTV monitors for the supervision of manually controlled barrier level crossings (Chapter 30).

A predictable and repetitive train service lends itself readily to the use of computer-controlled automatic route setting equipment (ARS), relieving the workload of signallers and allowing them to control larger areas. When introduced to work in conjunction with computer-based interlockings and VDUs, the Integrated Electronic Control Centre (IECC) was born. In signalling control centres fitted with ARS, routes are set by the computer as programmed, including decisions on priorities at junctions, and alterations in the case of late running and general service disruption. ARS has been enhanced since it was first introduced, and manual intervention by signallers is only required in exceptional circumstances.

Event and voice recorders

Event recorders are installed in all modern signal boxes and remote interlockings to record such things as the setting of routes, signal aspect changes, the lie of points, the occupation of track circuits, etc. This information is especially useful to incident investigators and may include a facility to display graphically the events leading up to the incident.

Voice recorders are also installed in all signal boxes – even those controlling absolute block signalling. These record any voice communications to or from signallers. Their purpose is to provide evidence in the event of incidents, and to provide a means of monitoring the standard of *safety critical communications*.

CHAPTER 17

Miscellaneous matters relating to track circuit block signalling

Signalling a passenger train into an occupied platform (permissive working)

Where the signalling arrangements allow, the signaller can signal a train into an already occupied platform (otherwise known as calling-on) by a method of working known as *permissive working* (see Chapter 14). To do so, the signaller will set the route in the normal way, but the main signal aspect will remain at red, owing to the occupation of a track circuit by a train in the route ahead. In such circumstances, authority for the driver to proceed will be given by two white lights inclined at 45° in the associated position light signal, as the train approaches the signal. These are the only circumstances in which the driver of a passenger train may proceed on the authority of a position light signal.

Where permissive working is in force at a through platform line, the platform starting signal must be at danger and the train ahead have completed its movement before clearance of the position light signal for the second train. This is to avoid the possibility of the second train entering the platform while the first train leaves it, with the trains not far apart, the cause of several collisions in the past.

Permissive working of this nature can be avoided in new installations by, for example, the provision of mid-platform signals on through platforms of sufficient length. However, such signals can be at heightened risk of being passed at danger if the driver is not expecting to have to stop at the mid-platform signal at danger. Such signals are also likely to have a very short overlap or none at all.

Lamp failures in colour light running signals (lamp proving)

Where colour light signals are fitted with filament lamps rather than LEDs, each lamp has both a main filament and an auxiliary filament. Any failure of a main filament causes an indication of the failure to be given in the signal box. If a lamp that should be illuminated fails completely, the next main running signal on the approach side will be maintained at red, in order to ensure safety.

Numbering of colour light signals

Each signal post carries a plate bearing the signal identity, comprising one or two prefix letters representing either the control centre, or the line of route, followed by a number unique to that prefix. Odd numbers are used for the down direction, with the numbers ascending in the direction of the traffic flow. Even numbers are used for the up direction, descending in the direction of the traffic flow. Automatic signals are identified as such to the driver by a horizontal black band on the identity plate. Semi-automatic signals carry the word 'SEMI' on the plate, above the horizontal band. Older installations may vary from the above.

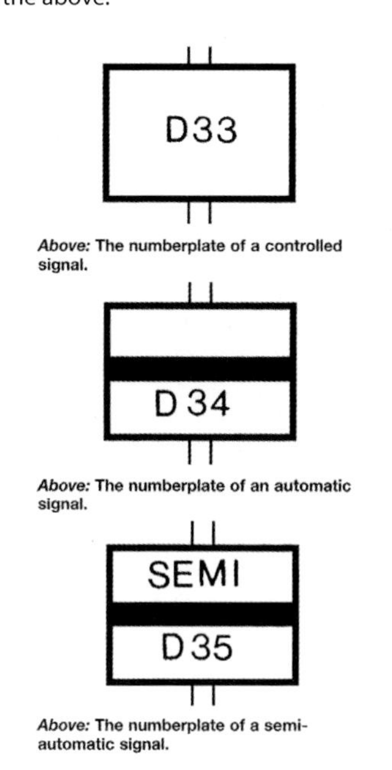

Above: The numberplate of a controlled signal.

Above: The numberplate of an automatic signal.

Above: The numberplate of a semi-automatic signal.

Signal identification plates

RIGHT A typical HW2000 electric point machine with back drive. This particular set of points has a lock stretcher bar and three other (yellow-painted) stretcher bars. The rods that connect the switch rails to the point machine are there to detect that they are in the correct position and are locked after having been driven across to the other position by the electric motor. *Author*

ABOVE Clamplock-operated points as fitted with a back drive. The grey box on the left-hand side of the picture is the hydraulic power pack and the yellow boxes on the outsides of each rail are the detection microswitches. The hydraulic actuator to move the switch rails is in the four-foot. *Author*

RIGHT The component parts of a set of points

Remote control standby arrangements

Standby arrangements, known as *override facilities*, are provided at the older power signal boxes to deal with any failure of the cable between the signal box and remote interlockings. These standby arrangements enable train movements to continue, but line capacity is reduced. In newer installations the control link (known as time-division multiplex, or TDM) is duplicated to avoid the provision of expensive override facilities and to reduce the disruption of train services.

Signals from sidings on to running lines

A main signal (rather than a position light signal) is provided at the exit from sidings where there are regular right-away movements and the next signal ahead is not visible from the siding exit (or is a long distance ahead).

Colour light signals not in use

When main or position light aspects are not in use they are covered over. A large 'X' may also be exhibited over the cover of main aspects.

Points

Unless worked from a ground frame, points on running lines signalled under the track circuit block arrangements are power-operated, usually by electric motor or by a hydraulically driven slide and clamp mechanism (usually known as a 'clamplock' and more suited to slower-speed locations). Some older installations used electro-pneumatic point machines, which were in widespread use at places like Birmingham New Street and London Euston.

The basic function of the point operating mechanism is to:

1. Move the point *switch blades*, which are connected together by *stretcher bars*, from one position to another
2. Detect that the switch blades are in the correct position against the appropriate *stock rail*
3. Lock the point blades so that they will not move under the passage of a train.

Most points are also fitted with a supplementary drive (*back drive)* to provide a mechanical drive from the point-operating mechanism to a position part way along the length of the switch blades in order to ensure that there is sufficient clearance for the wheel flanges to pass through the gap between the stock rail and the open switch rail on that side of the points.

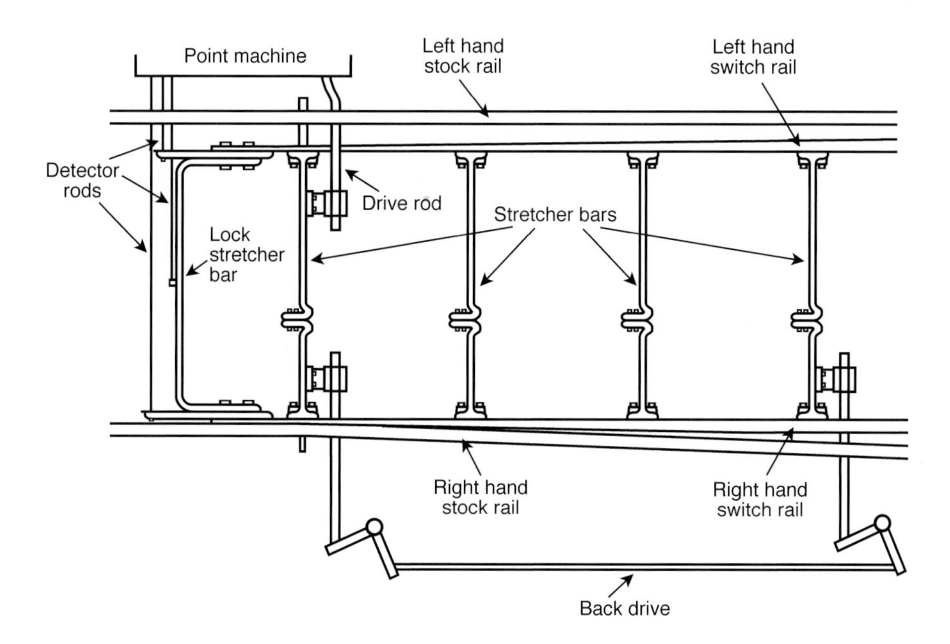

ABOVE LEFT HPSS points showing the electric drive arrangement and the tube down the middle of the four-foot, which is the torsional back drive. *Author*

ABOVE RIGHT Hy-Drive points, showing the in-bearer clamplocks and the supplementary drive in the four-foot. *Network Rail*

The signalling system will not permit a signal to show a proceed aspect unless the points in the route ahead to the next stop signal are 'set, locked and detected' as described in 1 to 3 above.

From the 1990s, new point-operating mechanisms have been developed:

1. The High Performance Switch System (HPSS), consisting of an electrically operated in-sleeper point machine, supplementary detectors and a torsional back drive.
2. The Hy-Drive point operating system, as fitted to the heavier-section 60kg/m rail now finding widespread use on main lines. The system is all hydraulic and consists of an in-bearer clamplock; an adjustable stretcher bar (based on a standard French Railways design); supplementary point drive and detection units (based on a design widely used on the Italian Rail network); and a hydraulic power pack. The Hy-Drive system has an advantage over the HPSS in that the back drive(s) positively lock(s) the switch blades in the required position(s). It is particularly suitable therefore for use on high-speed lines.

CHAPTER 18

Track circuit block signalling – failures and emergencies

Complete failure of signalling equipment

In the event of a complete failure of the signalling equipment affecting several signals along a substantial length of route, a substitute system of *temporary block working* may be introduced. In this method of working, *handsignallers* are appointed and there must be communication between them and the signaller. They are posted at signals at strategic locations and temporary block working is introduced between them, under the instructions of the signaller. The handsignaller completes a temporary block working ticket and gives it to the driver; the ticket may authorise the driver to pass two or more consecutive signals.

Track circuit irregularities

Track circuits are so designed that when they fail to operate correctly they *fail safe*, i.e. they switch protecting signals to danger and lock points, etc. Any failure that did not initiate such safeguards would be very serious; failures of that type (fortunately rare) are known as *wrongside failures*.

A signaller becomes aware of such an irregularity, commonly but incorrectly called a track circuit failure, when the red track circuit lights are illuminated on the panel, or displayed on a VDU, when there is no train on that section of the line, or when the red lights fail to go out after a train has passed and the following track circuit has cleared. The most likely cause is a failure of equipment, but the signaller must not assume that such is the cause. On the contrary, the signaller must assume that the line may be obstructed, and must use available means to find out whether it is or not. In the meantime, trains will be at a standstill because the protecting signal will be at red.

Unless the signaller can establish that the line is clear (e.g. by telephoning a station supervisor if the track circuit concerned is near the station), they must arrange for the line to be examined. It is usually most convenient for this to be done by using a train, and the driver must be informed of the circumstances, instructed to proceed cautiously over the affected portion of line, prepared to stop short of any obstruction, and to report any findings.

Any class of train may be used irrespective of the weather conditions, except that complications arise when any part of the track circuit is within a tunnel. A train may still be used for examination purposes, but the driver of the train is instructed to proceed with extreme caution, and not to exceed 16km/h (10mph) through the tunnel. Another train must not be allowed to pass through the tunnel while the line is being examined.

If it is established that there is no obstruction causing the track circuit to show occupied, it must be considered as having failed, and following trains may be allowed to proceed, each driver being authorised to pass the protecting signal at danger. However, while the failure exists, the signaller has no way of knowing whether the piece of line concerned is clear or not, and must therefore take one of two possible precautions:

1. Appoint someone suitable to stand at the track circuit to report whether it is clear after each train has passed
2. Carefully watch, on the panel or VDU, the passage of each train and see that it occupies and clears the track circuit ahead of the signal beyond the failed track circuit. Drivers must be instructed to proceed cautiously, because the signaller cannot be 100% sure that the line is clear.

Degraded mode signalling

In order to provide a safe means of allowing train movements in the event of a partial signalling failure, a *'proceed on sight authority'* (PoSA) has been introduced. This provides a distinctive alternative signal aspect that may be displayed when the main signal aspect cannot be cleared, for example because there has been a track circuit failure in the route ahead. It avoids the necessity of the signaller having to verbally authorise a driver to pass a signal at danger and is a safer arrangement because there is always a small risk of verbal instructions being misunderstood.

The PoSA proceed aspect is given by a flashing position light signal indicating that a *degraded movement* may take place to the next main stop signal. The driver may then proceed on the authority of the PoSA aspect but at such a speed that the train can stop short of any obstruction that may come into view.

Axle counter failures

Axle counters are subject to special arrangements to ensure that after the failure has been rectified the line ahead is safe for trains to run on. Axle counters are returned to service by a dual process of reset and restoration following which the section of line concerned must be subjected to the 'Examination of the line' procedure described below.

Examination of the line

If there is reason to believe, owing to some emergency or other, that the line may be blocked or unsafe to use, a train may be allowed to enter the section on any line in the right direction to examine it. The term 'examination of line' is not confined solely to the track itself but includes anything out of the ordinary that may endanger a train. It also includes all lines in the section concerned, not just the line on which the train is running. The precise Rule Book wording 'examine the line to see if it is safe for trains to pass' really means 'look out for any source of danger on any line'. Certain provisos have to be observed:

1. A train with a failed headlight must not be used during darkness or poor visibility or if there is a tunnel in the affected section (in case a train should run into an obstruction in poor visibility).
2. A train must not be allowed to enter a tunnel while the line is being examined by another train.

The driver of the examining train must be told about what is going on and instructed to proceed cautiously, ready to stop at any moment on seeing an obstruction or any other source of danger ahead. After the examining train has entered the affected section of line, drivers of trains on adjacent lines must be told what is happening and instructed to pass the affected section of line at caution and report anything seen to be wrong, until the signaller has received a report stating which lines are safe for trains to run on.

Suspected track defect

From time to time drivers feel a bump or jolt that is more severe than the usual bumps that are part and parcel of most journeys. They must then report the facts to the signaller so that following trains can be stopped, in case a dangerous defect has developed in the track, or it is obstructed in some way.

The signaller must then arrange for the line to be examined as described above. If no reason for the bump can be found, normal working may be resumed on other lines, but on the affected line drivers must be stopped and told about what has happened and instructed to proceed cautiously. This procedure must be continued for each following train until the affected line has been examined and confirmed to be safe by a person in charge of work on railway infrastructure and, if necessary, emergency speed restriction warning boards have been placed alongside the track on the approach to the defect. It is important that drivers reporting a bump should be as precise as possible regarding its location and at all costs avoid giving a misleading location. It is equally important that the track maintenance staff are sure that any defect they find is the one reported by the driver.

Suspected damage to track or structures

A train must not pass over a portion of line affected by subsidence or by suspected damage to a structure above or beneath the railway unless the signaller has been assured that it is safe for the train to do so, travelling at reduced speed if necessary.

If a railway bridge over a road has been hit by a road vehicle (an occurrence known as *bridge bashing*), trains must be stopped until the bridge has been examined. If a bridge examining engineer is not immediately available, the bridge may be examined by a bridge strike nominee. If the damage is only superficial, the bridge strike nominee may allow trains to pass over the bridge at 5mph (8km/h) in the case of a rail-over-road bridge, or up to 20mph (32km/h) where the bridge is over the railway, pending an examination by a bridge examining engineer.

Broken rails in continuous welded track

A broken rail may be detected in a number of ways:

1. If there is a gap between the two broken ends, any track circuit current flowing through the rail is interrupted, causing the track circuit indication on the signal box panel to show occupied, and switching the signal on the approach side to danger.
2. It may be noticed by the track patroller on a regular routine inspection, or by some other member of staff.
3. A driver passing over the spot may feel an unusual bump, and will stop and report it, prompting an examination of the track.

If a broken rail is reported to a signaller, all trains on the affected line must be stopped and arrangements made for a competent person (a rail defect examiner or rail defect nominee) to examine the rail concerned. The competent person may authorise trains to proceed over a broken or distorted rail at 5mph (8km/h) provided that certain conditions laid down by Network Rail are met.

The rail must be carefully examined before each train passes over it.While a train is passing over the break, no train may be allowed to pass over an adjoining line (a safety precaution in case the train passing over the break becomes derailed). Once action has been taken to secure the broken rail, usually with temporary clamps, and an emergency speed restriction has been put in place, these conditions may be relaxed.

PART 4

CHAPTER 19

Train protection

Introduction

The safety of railway operations is still greatly dependent on drivers correctly observing and responding to the signal aspects displayed. Although there are train protection systems installed on the network (described in more detail later), these are not 100% effective and if a driver passes a signal at danger without authority (a SPAD), there is the possibility of a collision occurring.

During the 1990s there was growing concern about the number of instances of signals being passed at danger. This was given emphasis by the serious collisions at Southall and Ladbroke Grove in 1997 and 1999 respectively, and from an increase, albeit slight, in the number of SPADs in 1998/99. Several initiatives were therefore taken to improve the position and SPAD numbers have reduced greatly since that time.

The most significant measure was the fitment of the Train Protection and Warning System (TPWS) to those signals at highest risk. This does not prevent SPAD incidents itself, but mitigates the consequences by stopping or slowing trains (depending on their approach speed and braking performance) before they can reach a point where they may collide with another train. Also, TPWS may well have had an effect in modifying driving behaviour to a more cautious style, reducing the number of SPAD incidents.

Other initiatives have included improved techniques to sight signals (known as *signal sighting*) and in the training of drivers. Train operating companies introduced 'defensive driving' policies requiring, for example, drivers to positively brake at the first cautionary signal aspect, to have reduced speed to 32km/h (20mph) by the AWS magnets and to stop 20 metres before a signal at danger. These measures are now deemed to be an inherent part of professional driving. There have also been major improvements to the way that drivers acquire route knowledge, including knowledge of those features along the route that a driver must particularly note such as a signal with a poor SPAD record.

A number of steps were also taken to give drivers prior warning that they were approaching a signal that did not have a good approach view and that they may come upon quite suddenly. Banner repeater signals, signs warning of a signal ahead and countdown markers of the type used approaching motorway exits have been provided in a number of cases.

Great care is now taken in the design and installation of signalling to:

1. Minimise the possibility of a driver failing to notice a signal and its aspect(s) by siting signals so that they can be clearly seen at defined distances away from them and will be in the driver's forward field of view (signal sighting is the process to achieve this).
2. Minimise the possibility of a collision should there be a SPAD incident by maximising the distance available before a collision could occur (known as the safe overrun distance). This may be done by setting the position of any points directly ahead of the signal to, if possible, divert the train away from harm. In many cases, this will not be possible.

TPWS is installed at those signals where it has the greatest benefit in stopping an overrunning train before it can reach another on a conflicting route. It is legal requirement that TPWS is installed at *junction protecting signals,* but it has also been fitted more widely. TPWS supplements the earlier Automatic Warning System (AWS), which is basically an advisory system.

Completely eliminating the consequences of driver error requires the more comprehensive train protection system, Automatic Train Protection (ATP). ATP has been fitted to two routes and is an inherent part of the European Train Control System (ETCS), the signalling element of the European Traffic Management System (ERTMS). Over time, ATP will protect most of the rail network as ETCS/ERTMS is progressively fitted to it.

For any train protection system to be completely effective, not only does the equipment need to be fitted to the track, but it must also be fitted to all the trains running on the route. Even then, it will not protect against the effects of low adhesion in which the wheels fail to grip the rails during braking, which can result in a long overrun. The management of low adhesion is a subject in itself, and beyond the scope of this book.

Where tilting trains run on the network, a system has had to be introduced to ensure that this can be done safely. This is achieved by fitting the Tilt Advisory and Supervisory System (TASS) to the track and the trains (chapter 25).

CHAPTER 20

Responsibilities of railway staff in the observance of signals

Signals are the means by which the driver receives instructions from the signaller. In addition to stop, caution and clear, however, there are other factors to be considered if safety is to be achieved.

In the following, the term 'guard' is synonymous with conductor, train manager, etc.

Observance of signals

When a train stops on the approach to a signal showing a proceed aspect (at a station platform, for example) the driver must look at the signal again before restarting, in case the signaller has replaced it to danger in the meantime either in an emergency or to give priority to another train. In the latter case the signaller must not clear the signals for a conflicting movement until it has been confirmed that the driver of the first train has noticed that the signal has been replaced.

If drivers find that a junction signal is cleared for the wrong route, they must stop at the signal if it is safe and practicable to do so, and speak to the signaller.

In areas of absolute block signalling, if a train is stopped, or nearly stopped, before the clearance of a stop signal, this may be a warning to the driver that the next signal may also be at danger. The signals are worked in this way in order to avoid any risk of the driver failing to observe the next signal, should it be at danger.

Doubt as to signal aspect

In the following circumstances a driver must treat a stop signal as being at danger (or a distant signal at caution):

1. No signal, where there should be one
2. No light in a signal
3. At a colour light signal, where there is doubt as to which aspect applies
4. A semaphore signal at 'half-cock' (neither on nor off; after dark this may cause a part green/ part red light to be displayed)
5. A white light, where there should be a coloured light
6. One light is showing in a position-light or subsidiary signal where there should be two

The driver must immediately inform the signaller, stopping specially to do so, if necessary. The driver must also do so if any irregularity in the working of signals is encountered, or an irregular aspect sequence, and complete the appropriate report form.

Authority to pass a signal at danger

There are several circumstances in which this may occur, the authority being given personally to the driver by the signaller or other nominated person. Before starting, the driver must reset the *Driver's Reminder Appliance* (DRA) (covered later in this chapter), if fitted; press the TPWS override button (if the signal is fitted with TPWS); give one long blast on the horn; then proceed cautiously at such reduced speed as will enable the train to stop clear of any obstruction. The driver must always be able to stop within the distance that the line can be seen to be clear; it is better to incur delay than risk a collision.

The driver must, if possible, observe any facing points to see that they are in the correct position, and pass through them at not more than 24km/h (15mph).

If the driver sees the next stop signal ahead showing a proceed aspect, it must not be assumed that the line ahead is clear. The signal may be for a train in front.

Train detained at a signal at danger

In years past, many serious accidents occurred when the signaller forgot about a train standing at a semaphore signal without a berth track circuit. In such circumstances, the driver was required to go to the signal box to speak to and remind the signaller that the train was there. The driver was also required to sign the *train register book*.

Now that train detection systems, such as track circuits or axle counters, are fitted widely across the rail network, the danger of a signaller overlooking the presence of a train should no longer exist, but it is still necessary for the driver of a train detained at a signal to speak to the signaller in case the latter wishes to give him a message.

The driver should use the *GSM-R radio* as the normal method of speaking to the signaller. He must speak to the signaller as soon as it is possible to do so, the only exception to this being if there is an obvious reason for the signal being at danger, such as an obvious conflicting train movement ahead. In this case the driver may wait 2 minutes before contacting the signaller, and must then contact the signaller again at intervals of 5 minutes if the train continues to be detained.

If the train radio system is not available for some reason, and a *signal post telephone* is fitted to the signal concerned, the driver should use it to contact the signaller. This is housed in a cabinet indicated by a black and white diagonally striped sign.

Where there is a yellow or white diamond sign with the letter 'X' at the signal, or where there is a sign showing a black cross on a white background with a yellow roundel superimposed on it on the telephone cabinet, the driver must not leave the cab to use the telephone except in emergency. The driver must stay in the cab until the signal clears, or until advised that the signaller has blocked the next line and it is safe to leave the cab to use the telephone. This procedure is in force at places where there are several running lines close together, resulting in limited clearance, and the driver would be in danger if he left the cab to use the telephone.

If there is no telephone at the signal, such as on lines not equipped with track circuit block, but there is a white diamond sign indicating that the presence of the train is detected by the signalling system, the driver should try using a mobile telephone if unable to contact the signaller by using the train radio system. If the driver still cannot contact the signaller, either a signal or lineside telephone should be located, or the signal box visited. In some cases, the telephone number of the signal box is displayed on a plate on the signal post under the white diamond sign. At these signals the driver may only leave the driving cab to use another telephone in an emergency, or when advised that train movements on the adjacent line have been stopped so that it is safe to leave the cab.

If there is no white diamond sign at the signal on a non-track circuit block line, and the visibility is less than 180 metres (200 yards), such as during fog or falling snow, the driver must attempt to contact the signaller immediately.

Shunting movement detained on a running line

If a shunting movement is detained for an unreasonably long time on a running line, the driver must remind the signaller in the quickest way possible. This may mean that the driver or the shunter has to go to the signal box to do so.

The Driver's Reminder Appliance (DRA) and guard's duties

Drivers have long been aware of the possibility of inadvertently starting away against platform starting signals at danger, caused in part by the incorrect receipt of the 'Ready to start' bell signal from the guard, and some drivers had their own method of reminding themselves that the platform starting signal is at danger. This has now been regularised by the provision of a reminder appliance in the form of a large button that the driver must depress when stopped at a signal at danger. When depressed, the button illuminates red and prevents traction power from being applied until the button is pulled out.

In this form, the device known as the Driver's Reminder Appliance (DRA) is fitted to the driver's cabs of all passenger trains. The DRA must be set whenever a train stops at a signal at danger, and reset when the signal clears. It must also be set when the train stops at a station where no signal is provided, after the train has passed the previous signal when at caution. This is to remind the driver that the signal ahead (which may be out of sight) may still be at danger.

As an additional safety measure, the guard must check (where practicable) that the platform starting signal has been cleared before giving the 'Ready to start' signal to the driver. The same arrangement applies to a person in charge of a platform, before a handsignal is given to the guard to indicate that station work is complete

LEFT These signals at Birmingham New Street station control train movements from both sides of an island platform. The 'RA' stencil meaning 'right away' has been illuminated by the person in charge of train dispatch to indicate to the driver that is safe for the train to depart. It should be noted that the equipment will prevent the RA illuminating unless the signal is also displaying a proceed aspect. *Author*

or the 'Ready to start' signal is given to the driver of a driver-only train.

Where a *right away indicator*, displaying the letters 'RA' when operated, is provided, the indication will not be displayed until the platform starting signal is cleared. This is an important safeguard against a mistake being made by the guard in giving the right-away signal with the starting signal at danger.

The signaller's actions

If a train passes a signal at danger without authority, the signaller must immediately arrange for the train to be stopped and take any other necessary emergency action. The signaller must speak to the driver and ask a number of questions printed on a SPAD report form. Details must be given to operations control and the signaller must not allow the train to proceed without its authority. If there is any doubt about the correct working of a signal it must be treated as being defective.

SPAD alarms are provided in signalling control centres to alert the signaller and give an immediate audible alarm and visual message when a signal is passed at danger. The visual message displays the identification numbers of the signal and train concerned.

CHAPTER 21

Signal sighting

Signal sighting (the driver's approach view of signals) is a very important factor when determining the precise location of new signals, and for investigating the reasons why a signal has been passed at danger, possibly repeatedly. It is equally important when changes in the surroundings of signals may impede the driver's view of them. Such changes may result from, for example, building work, the growth of lineside vegetation and the installation of overhead electrification.

Signal siting is the expression used to denote where the signals are located.

When approaching a signal, a driver has to interpret the aspects displayed in order to control the train accordingly. Complex signal arrangements such as gantries require more time to do this, leading to the concept of the *reading time* necessary. The current standard is for signals to have a minimum reading time, which for a simple lineside signal is generally a minimum of 8 seconds (less may be allowed in certain circumstances) when approaching at line speed. This means that drivers must be able to see the signal at least 8 seconds before passing it. The more complicated the signalling arrangement, the greater is the minimum reading time that must be provided. Part of the process of signal sighting is to determine the minimum reading time and assess how it should be provided in practice. Where reasonable to do so, the minimum reading time should be increased further if this can be achieved easily by, for example, the removal of lineside vegetation.

Signal sighting is carried out by committees set up for the purpose and their work will be carried out by site visits and by viewing desktop simulations of what the proposed signalling might look like. They must determine exactly where new signals should be sited, and whether any changes should be made to existing signals whose sighting is in question for any reason (for example following a SPAD incident). A committee consists of a chairman and a number of people who are competent in engineering and train driver requirements, including a competent representative of a train operating company operating over the route.

Sighting considerations are paramount, and the following factors must be borne in mind:

1. The type of signal and the method of displaying the signal head (e.g. straight post, angled post, gantry, etc)
2. Assessment of the minimum reading time and the effect of interruptions present during that time
3. The red aspect should be as near as possible to the driver's eye level
4. The centre of the light beam should generally be aligned towards a point 3 metres (10 feet) above the left-hand running rail at 180 metres (200 yards) from the signal (i.e. where the AWS magnets are usually located)
5. The desirability of providing banner or co-acting signals

Other factors to be borne in mind are:

RIGHT A typical gantry signal whose curved approach can cause problems for drivers in identifying the correct signal. To assist drivers, it may be noted that the middle signal on the gantry has a line reminder sign fitted displaying the letter 'T', meaning 'through line' (as opposed to one that passes by a platform). *Author*

1. Where practicable, the avoidance of sites on viaducts, steep gradients, in tunnels, across level crossings, or part-train length beyond a platform
2. The position of neutral sections on overhead electrified lines and conductor rail gaps on third rail electrified lines, to avoid the risk of trains being brought to a stand on 'dead' sections
3. The avoidance of environmental nuisance to lineside neighbours near signals at which trains are regularly stopped, caused by the noise of trains braking or accelerating, or the sound of engines idling or compressors working
4. The possibility of vandalism to trains or signalling equipment
5. The possibility of pilfering from stationary freight trains

Risk assessment of signals

All signals that protect junctions have been risk-assessed using a tool known as the *signal assessment tool*. The outcome is a numerical value that determines whether any further action needs to be considered to reduce the consequences if a SPAD occurs. Signals whose score is above a benchmark figure must be specially considered by an expert group to see what further measures, in addition to existing TPWS, could be provided. Such measures could include changes to signalling controls in the form of *robust train protection* (Chapter 23).

Risk assessment is complementary to signal sighting. It is focused on minimising the consequences of a SPAD should one occur, whereas the objective of signal sighting is to minimise the likelihood of a signal being passed at danger in the first place.

Platform starting signals

A number of serious accidents occurred in the past when drivers departed from a station and wrongly passed the platform starting signal when it was at danger (known as a *start against signal SPAD*, SASSPAD). Protection against this risk is now most effectively provided by TPWS and to a lesser extent by the Driver's Reminder Appliance, described earlier.

A variant of the SASSPAD is the *start on yellow SPAD*, or SOYSPAD. This problem arises when a train starts from a platform starting signal displaying a single yellow aspect, which means that the next signal ahead at that time will be at danger. In these circumstances, a driver must always remember the possibility of having to stop at the first signal, and control the train's speed accordingly. A SOYSPAD may occur if the driver forgets the aspect shown by the platform starting signal and continues to accelerate; by the time the next signal comes into view, the train may be going too fast to be able to stop in time and the signal may be protecting a junction. TPWS may not be a fully effective measure in these circumstances.

Good approach visibility of platform starting signals from the driver's position is essential if the likelihood of a SPAD is to be minimised. To provide this, the stopping point for trains is now typically 25 metres (28 yards) before the starting signal, where the length of the platform allows. For new signalling schemes, this may require platforms to be lengthened. Another measure that can help the driver is the provision of miniature repeating signals at cab height.

Before the introduction of TPWS, certain locations where there was a particularly high risk of collision if a signal was passed at danger were provided with *SPAD indicators,* and these were not removed when TPWS was fitted. They are similar to a normal three-aspect colour light signal and located about 50 metres (55 yards) beyond the signal concerned.

SPAD indicators normally display no aspect, but when the signal to which they refer is passed at danger they immediately display the following aspects: the top and bottom aspects flash red and the centre aspect displays a steady red light. The driver must stop at once and tell the signaller what has happened. The driver must also stop the train and report to the signaller if a SPAD indicator is seen to be flashing for a signal on another line. This is a safety precaution in case the train is on a collision course with the other.

A SPAD indicator may also have an AWS magnet positioned on its approach. It is suppressed for normal signalled movements, but will give an AWS warning when the SPAD indicator is triggered.

CHAPTER 22

The Automatic Warning System (AWS)

AWS was approved for use on British Railways in 1956, since when it has been installed on almost all of Britain's total route mileage of approximately 16,000km. Its simple purpose is to remind a driver to slow down or stop. If the driver fails to acknowledge such a reminder, the brakes will automatically be applied within 2 or 3 seconds.

Track equipment

A permanent magnet and an electro-magnet are installed between the rails (known as the *four-foot*), normally about 180 metres (200 yards) on the approach side of a signal that can display at least a caution or preliminary caution aspect. On the West Coast Main Line, this distance was increased to 230 metres (260 yards), but was not adopted on other lines where permissible speeds are greater than 160km/h (100mph).

On lines that are not electrified using direct current in conductor rails, the magnets are painted yellow. In DC-electrified areas, the AWS magnets have to be of greater strength to overcome the magnetic flux from the conductor rail, and are painted green.

A permanent magnet only is provided on the approach to *permanent speed restriction* warning boards (sometimes known as Morpeth boards) where the approach speed is greater than 96km/h (60mph) and the reduction in speed required is a third or more. Portable permanent magnets are also provided on the approach to temporary speed restrictions and emergency speed restrictions.

Locomotive or multiple unit equipment

A receiver is fitted underneath each end of a locomotive or multiple unit, and it reacts to the magnets fitted to the track. A bell and a horn (or an electronic representation) are provided in the cab, together with an acknowledgement button and a visual indicator.

Method of operation

When a signal displays a clear (or green) aspect, the electro-magnet is energised. This causes the bell in the driving cab to give a short ring, and

ABOVE LEFT A standard AWS magnet showing (left) the permanent magnet, immediately followed by the electro-magnet. The electro-magnet is only energised when the related signal is showing a green aspect. In the background may be seen part of an axle counter head and its connections. *Author*

BELOW LEFT A high-strength AWS magnet for use on lines fitted with conductor rails, and distinguished from standard magnets by being painted green. *Author*

the visual indicator to show all black. No action is required by the driver.

In all other cases the electro-magnet is inoperative. When a train passes over the permanent magnet the horn will sound a warning, and unless the driver presses the acknowledgement button within 2-3 seconds (which will silence the horn) an emergency application of the brake will be made. The visual indicator will show all black until the acknowledgement button is pressed, after which it will display a segmented disc, coloured alternately black and yellow (often named the '*sunflower*'), as a reminder to the driver that a warning has been acknowledged and the automatic brake application has been overridden. The responsibility for applying the brake is now the driver's.

ABOVE The interior of an HST driving cab showing the AWS reset button (bottom centre) and the AWS 'sunflower' under the number '43135'. Also to be seen is the mushroom-headed 'Driver's Reminder Appliance' illuminated red (centre left) – see Chapter 20 – and the 'Energymiser' Driver's Advisory System on the right of the picture. *Peter van der Mark*

Summary of warnings

Where AWS equipment is provided, the warning horn sounds when the train is approaching the following:

1. A colour light signal displaying any of these aspects: red, single yellow, double yellow, flashing single yellow, flashing double yellow
2. A semaphore distant signal at caution
3. A warning sign for a permanent speed restriction
4. A warning sign for a temporary speed restriction
5. A warning sign for a speed restriction imposed without notice in an emergency
6. A cancelling indicator on a single line for trains moving in the opposite direction to which the signal applies
7. A *warning board* in connection with locally monitored level crossings (Chapter 30), where the train driver has to check an indicator showing that the flashing red road traffic signals are working properly before driving the train over the crossing
8. A signal displaying a clear aspect, alongside which has been placed a warning sign or indicator referring to a temporary or emergency speed restriction
9. A splitting distant signal that is at clear for the diverging route.

Operation over bi-directional lines

Where trains operate over lines in both directions, there are three options for fitting AWS track equipment:

1. If the signal spacing will allow it, an electro-magnet relating to two signals, each applying in the opposite direction, can be fitted either side of the permanent magnet.
2. Fitting a suppressor magnet coil to the permanent magnet so that when energised it suppresses the field from the permanent

magnet when a train is travelling in the opposite direction to which it applies. Then the driver will not receive a warning that does not apply.

3. A cheaper arrangement is to provide a cancelling indicator just beyond the AWS magnets applicable to movements in the opposite direction to which the magnets apply. This is a sign consisting of a white St Andrew's cross on a blue background and advises drivers to cancel the AWS warning without needing to take any further action.

AWS gaps

Sometimes AWS equipment is not provided at large stations where speeds are low, even though the approach lines are equipped. The start of the AWS gap is indicated by a circular white sign showing 'AWS' with a red cross. The end is indicated by a square white sign showing 'AWS'.

In some places AWS equipment is not provided for trains travelling in the wrong direction on a bi-directional line. The start of the AWS gap is indicated by a diamond-shaped white sign showing 'AWS' with a red cross. The end is indicated by the same sign without the red cross.

Failures and irregularities

If the bell sounds in circumstances in which the horn should sound (or if there is no sound), there is a wrongside failure, and the driver must tell the signaller at once, stopping specially if necessary, so that other drivers can be warned.

If there is a rightside failure (a horn, or no indication, when there should have been a bell), the driver must tell the signaller at the first convenient opportunity, so that the defect can be repaired.

AWS isolation

A locomotive or unit must not enter service if the AWS is *isolated* (i.e. out of use) in any driving cab that is required to be used, or if the seal is broken on an AWS isolating handle. The meaning of the term 'in service' means a train that is ready to start a journey. A train is out of service at the end of a journey or reversing point. The term 'journey' means a journey between a station (or depot or siding) and another station (or depot or siding). A journey finishes where a train has to reverse, or have vehicles attached or detached.

If, while in service, the pressing of the acknowledgement button does not stop the sounding of the horn, or does not prevent the brakes from being applied, the driver must isolate the AWS, then tell the signaller and not move the train until instructed to do so. The signaller must advise operations control at once.

The driver will be told of the arrangements that are being made. If a competent person is available to accompany the driver and stop the train in an emergency, the train may proceed normally to a nominated point. If no such person is available the train may proceed to a nominated point at a maximum speed of 40mph (64km/h).

Very detailed and comprehensive instructions for dealing with AWS failures arose following the serious accident at Southall on 19 September 1997 in which the AWS was isolated in the leading cab, and in which six people were killed.

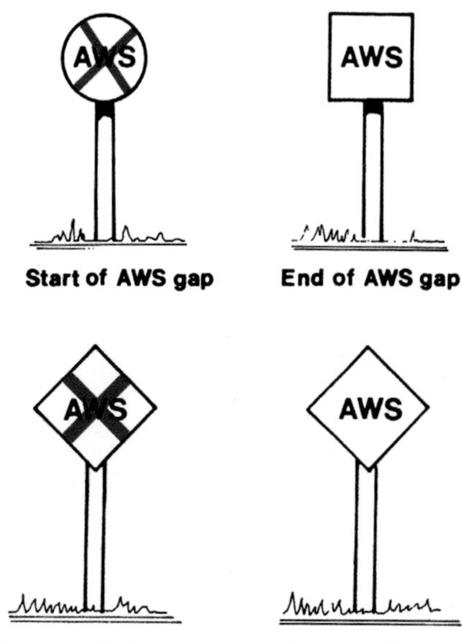

RIGHT Signs showing the start and finish of AWS gaps, usually at a low-speed station

BELOW RIGHT Signs showing the start and finish of AWS gaps for trains travelling in the wrong direction on a bi-directional line.

CHAPTER 23

The Train Protection and Warning System (TPWS)

TPWS was developed as an enhancement of AWS when it was decided not to proceed with Automatic Train Protection (Chapter 24). TPWS does not prevent signals from being passed at danger, but is designed to reduce the possible consequences if such an event occurs. It is designed to cover the eventuality of a driver acknowledging the AWS warning at a caution signal, then failing to apply the brake. It also incorporates a train stop that applies the brake immediately if a driver passes a signal at danger, which is a very valuable safeguard in the case of platform starting signals. As a legal requirement, TPWS must be provided:

1. At signals protecting junctions, i.e. those protecting crossovers or conflicting areas of movement
2. On the approach to buffer stops at passenger platforms
3. On the approach to most permanent speed restrictions where the approach speed is 60mph (96km/h) or more and the reduction in speed is at least one third (i.e. those that are provided with permanent AWS magnets)

TPWS does not provide the same degree of protection as ATP, but it had the great benefit of being able to be installed in a much shorter time-scale and at a much lower cost. Signals protecting junctions are about 40% of the total number, and experience has shown that passing these signals is most likely to result in accidents. Following the very serious collision at Ladbroke Grove on 5 October 1999 caused by a SPAD, there was an urgency to have TPWS installed as soon as possible, and Railtrack achieved this by the end of 2002, a year before the Regulations required it. Where TPWS is installed the existing AWS continues to operate normally.

Track equipment

At most fitted signals, the track equipment consists of a pair of loops either arranged as an *overspeed sensor* (sometimes known as a *speed trap*) on the approach to the signal, or a *train stop sensor* at the signal (some signals such as platform starting signals are only fitted with a train stop sensor). The loops are only energised when the signal is at danger and radiate specific frequencies that are picked up by a passing train. The system is not therefore fail-safe because the

LEFT Pairs of TPWS train stop sensors are fitted to signals CR92 and CR94 at Chester. Should a train pass either of these signals at danger, the system will apply an immediate emergency brake application. Where configured as an overspeed sensor on the approach to a signal, permanent speed restriction or terminal platform buffer stops, the sensors are separated, the amount of separation determining the trip speed. *Author*

RIGHT Typical TPWS overspeed sensor loops on the approach to buffer stops. Special 'mini' loops had to be developed for the platform application to avoid the system applying an emergency brake application at less than the intended set speed. *Author*

protection is lost if the loops fail to energise (e.g. a cable may have been cut, accidentally or as a result of vandalism).

However, a monitoring system is provided and if a loops fails to transmit as required the previous signal will be held at danger.

The overspeed sensor initiates an emergency brake application if a train approaches a TPWS-fitted signal at danger at such a speed that the signal is likely to be passed. The precise location of the overspeed sensor and its speed setting depend on the gradient and certain features regarding the track and signalling layout ahead, but is likely to be within the range 90 to 450 metres (100 to 500 yards) before the signal. As there is normally a 180-metre (200-yards) overlap beyond colour light signals, TPWS should ensure that a train with good braking characteristics (at least 12% g), which is travelling at up to 75mph (120km/h) and has triggered the overspeed sensor, will be stopped within the overlap.

In many cases, protection will be effective for approach speeds greater than 75mph (120km/h) and braking worse than 12% g because the junction ahead where conflicting movements can occur is further from the signal than the overlap distance. This distance is called the *safe overrun distance*.

The overspeed sensor consists of an arming loop and a trigger loop. The arming loop causes a timer to be started in the TPWS equipment on the train, and if the trigger loop is reached before the timer has expired an emergency brake application will result; the spacing of the two loops therefore determines the set speed. Different timer settings are used on freight locomotives to enhance the effectiveness of TPWS, since their braking capabilities are poorer than those of passenger trains. The two different timer settings used are 0.974 second for passenger trains, and 1.218 seconds for freight trains.

The train stop sensor initiates an emergency brake application if the train passes a TPWS-fitted signal at danger. In this case, the arming and trigger loops are adjacent to each other with no separation. An override device is provided to inhibit the operation of the brake if the driver is authorised to pass the signal at danger.

Trainborne equipment

The trainborne equipment consists of an aerial located underneath the traction unit, together with a TPWS Electronics Unit incorporating the AWS equipment.

Operation of TPWS

TPWS may operate on the approach to a signal at danger while the driver is already braking, in which case it is known as an 'activation'. Where a driver is not already braking, the operation of TPWS is known as an 'intervention'. In addition to the immediate emergency brake application, the operation of TPWS causes an AWS warning to occur and a red indicator light known as a 'brake demand light' to flash on the TPWS panel in the driver's cab.

One weakness of TPWS is that, once having come to a stand, the driver can reset the system and carry on. The driver may do this if it has not been realised that a TPWS operation has occurred, or in the mistaken belief that the train needs to clear a junction that it may have stopped foul of. To counter this, the instructions are very clear that a driver must always consider that an emergency brake application could be caused by operation of the TPWS, and should not move the train afterwards without the permission of the signaller. Also, on new train builds, enhanced driver indications are required so that the driver should be in no doubt as to the cause of a brake demand.

Increasing the level of protection given by TPWS

Protection for train speeds in excess of 75mph (120km/h) can be obtained by providing an additional overspeed sensor further back from the signal. This is known as TPWS+. TPWS has also been fitted to a few plain-line signals that do not protect those junctions that have been specifically identified as being higher risk. This may include signals that protect level crossings where there is sufficient overrun distance to provide protection.

If TPWS+ is insufficient to stop a train in the safe overrun distance, the level of protection can be increased further by fitting additional TPWS to the signal before that protecting the junction (the junction protecting signal). This is known as robust train protection and this (outer) signal is then controlled so that it will only show an unrestricted proceed aspect if the route is set forward from the junction protecting signal, or if the train has slowed down sufficiently on the approach to the outer signal to be considered to be under control, in which case the outer signal will clear to allow it to move up to the junction protecting signal.

Where there are facing points beyond the junction protecting signal, the safe overrun distance can be increased by altering the signalling controls so that any train overrunning the signal will be diverted along a route where the consequences are likely to be the least severe (flank protection).

Has TPWS been effective?

TPWS appears to have been highly successful in reducing the number of SPAD-related accidents, SPAD incidents themselves and the risk of SPADs. At the time of publication, there had not been a SPAD-related fatal accident since that at Ladbroke Grove in October 1999, a period of more than 16 years. Prior to TPWS, the fatal accident rate was about one every 15 months. However, there is still a residual level of SPAD risk, so a collision as a result of a SPAD incident could still occur. Indeed, there have been several near misses following a SPAD, which could very easily have resulted in collision. The railway industry must therefore still continue its fight against SPADs.

There has also been a very significant reduction in buffer-stop collisions since TPWS was fitted to terminal platforms in stations.

CHAPTER 24

Automatic Train Protection (ATP)

Automatic Train Protection (ATP) is a more sophisticated system than the Automatic Warning System (AWS) and Train Protection and Warning System (TPWS) described in Chapters 22 and 23. AWS warns the driver when the train needs to reduce speed or stop, either for a speed restriction or a signal at danger. Furthermore, it checks that the driver has actually received the warning, because unless the driver acknowledges the warning by pressing a button, the brakes will be applied automatically. TPWS is fitted to those signals that have been identified as at highest risk, but the degree of protection given depends on the distance to the point where conflicting movements can occur, as well as the approach speed and a train's braking capability. There is also nothing to stop a driver continuing once the train has been stopped following the operation of TPWS.

AWS has been invaluable in raising safety standards on Britain's railways, but it is not designed to check that the driver is actually responding to the warning that has been acknowledged and is applying the brakes appropriately. It might be thought that such provision would be unnecessary on the grounds that, if sufficiently alert to acknowledge receiving the warning by the physical act of pressing a button, the driver will also be sufficiently alert to apply the brakes. However, there is now a substantial body of experience to show that this is not always the case, and several serious accidents have occurred in which drivers have pressed the acknowledgement button but have then failed to brake correctly, or even at all.

Since TPWS was installed, the level of protection against SPADs has been raised substantially, and it is almost certainly the case that a number of collisions have been avoided because a signal that was passed at danger was fitted with TPWS. However, the weaknesses of TPWS have been mentioned earlier.

ATP does not have the weaknesses of AWS and TPWS. Two pilot ATP schemes were introduced in 1991, from different manufacturers, one on the Great Western Main Line between Paddington and Bristol, and a second on the Chiltern line from Marylebone to Aynho Junction. The trials were more technically demanding, costly and prolonged than was expected, and eventually in 1995 the then Secretary of State for Transport decided that ATP should not be extended to other routes on the grounds that the expenditure was not justified – that is, that it would not be cost-effective. The system ought properly to be described as the BR-ATP system, as it differs in some respects from the subsequently developed European Train Control System (see Chapter 26). Attention was then concentrated on developing TPWS instead.

Initially, BR-ATP works in a similar way to AWS and TPWS. The train picks up messages from the track electronically, which tell the driver whether to slow down or stop. But the ATP system then goes on to check that the driver is actually reducing speed to the extent required. If it finds that this is not happening, it reminds the driver by giving a short visual and audible warning, and if that warning is unheeded by the driver ATP will apply the brakes.

This back-check is performed by an on-board computer, which on receipt of the warning calculates the rate of deceleration (known as the *braking curve*) that would be necessary to bring the train safely to a stand at a signal at danger (or reduce the speed to the level required by a speed restriction). The computer continuously checks the actual speed of the train against the braking curve that it has calculated, and gives a warning if it finds that the actual speed is higher than that demanded by the braking curve, followed if necessary by an application of the brake. A distance-measuring tachometer enables the computer to calculate the location of the train relative to the approaching signal.

ATP also safeguards the maximum permitted train speed throughout the journey by monitoring the actual train speed and checking it against the permitted speed. If the permitted speed is exceeded, ATP will intervene to cause speed to be reduced.

ABOVE An ATP track-mounted antenna. *Peter van der Mark*

Track equipment

At each signal, or at braking distance from a speed restriction, a track antenna is laid in the track and transmits the following information to the train via a receiver antenna fixed underneath the locomotive or multiple unit:

1. The distance to the next signal at danger, or to a speed restriction
2. The current maximum permitted speed at the beacon
3. The value and length of the next speed restriction, if there is one
4. The gradient

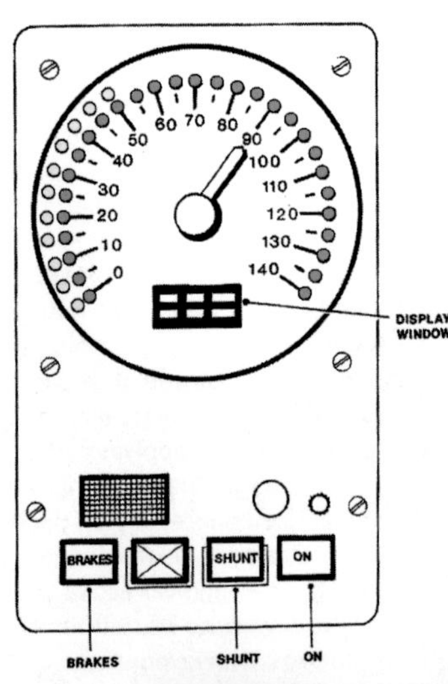

RIGHT The ATP speedometer showing green LEDs and yellow LEDs around the periphery

BELOW LEFT An unrefurbished Great Western Railway HST driving cab showing the BR-ATP speedometer towards the right-hand side of the picture. *Peter van der Mark*

BELOW RIGHT A detailed view of a BR-ATP speedometer. *Peter van der Mark*

Train equipment
Certain information on board trains that does not alter their performance may be permanently programmed into the on-board computer, such as the length and maximum permitted speed of a multiple unit. In other cases, before starting the journey the driver inputs the maximum permitted speed of the train, its type, length and braking capability. This information, together with that received from beacons, enables the on-board computer to calculate the appropriate braking curve.

Cab display
The main item of cab display is the ATP speedometer. Around the periphery of the dial are green light-emitting diodes (LEDs) at 5mph (8km/h) intervals, any one of which may be illuminated to show the maximum permitted speed, or flash to show a target speed ahead. Alongside these, from 0mph to 50mph (80km/h), are yellow LEDs, which have a 'release speed' function. A display window in the speedometer gives the driver a form of 'countdown' to the signal at danger.

Method of operation
When the train is approaching a double yellow signal, the green LED display, showing the maximum permitted speed, will change to a single flashing green LED at 0mph, and a short 'blip' tone will sound. The display window will show '0', meaning 'Stop at the next signal but two'. When the train passes the double yellow signal, the display window will change to '00', meaning 'Stop at the next signal but one'. When the train passes the single yellow signal, the display window will change to '000', meaning 'Stop at the next signal'.

Throughout this process, the train's actual speed will be compared with the braking curve calculated by the computer. If the driver fails to brake sufficiently, a warble tone will sound, the indicator in the display window will flash, and the green LED will go out. If the driver allows the ATP system to intervene and apply the brakes, it will be impossible to release them until speed has been reduced to 40mph (64km/h).

As far as speed restrictions are concerned, the procedure is somewhat similar. Approaching a speed restriction, say 40mph (64km/h), the steady green LED showing the maximum permitted speed will be replaced by a flashing green 40mph LED display, and a short 'blip' tone will sound. If the driver brakes correctly, the flashing LED will change to a steady 40mph display at the start of the speed restriction, and this indication will be maintained until the rear of the train has cleared the end of the speed restriction (hence the need for the driver to input the length of the train).

In order to carry out its functions without constantly interfering with the driver's handling of the train, the on-board ATP computer calculates three curves – the braking curve, the 'warning curve' and the 'intervention curve'. The warning curve, which gives a visual and audible warning to the driver when its speed is exceeded, has a tolerance of 3mph (5km/h) above the braking curve. Similarly, the intervention curve has a 3mph (5km/h) tolerance above the warning curve and will apply the brakes if this is exceeded. The curves are calculated to achieve the required speed at the commencement of a speed restriction, or to bring the train safely to a stand in the case of a signal being at danger.

Track equipment – placed intermittently or laid continuously
The main advantage of continuously laid track equipment is that it will update the signal information the instant an aspect changes. This means that the driver can start to accelerate as soon as a signal ahead changes to a less restrictive aspect, even though it may not be in sight. It also provides an added safeguard if a signal out of sight changes to a more restrictive aspect in an emergency. This gives the driver more time to stop. The main disadvantage of continuously laid track equipment is its cost.

Intermittent track equipment is cheaper, but if it is only provided at signals (and speed restrictions) the computer is not updated until the next beacon, and the signal ahead may be in the driver's view for a considerable distance. If the driver has just passed a single yellow signal when the signal ahead changes from red to a proceed aspect, the driver cannot accelerate, but must continue to brake as though the signal were still at red, because that is what the on-board computer still believes. Such slow running may not be acceptable in heavily worked areas, especially at junctions.

These delays can be reduced in two ways:

1. By providing additional 'fill-in' beacons between signals at critical locations, so that the computer can be updated sooner
2. By allowing the driver to override the computer when the signal in sight ahead changes from red, and speed has been reduced to a sufficiently low level, known as the *release speed*. This may appear to be less than entirely satisfactory from a safety point of view, but the release speed chosen for Britain's railways is sufficiently low that a train can be stopped safely within the overlap of the signal at red, should the driver attempt to go past it in error. If the train were to pass a red signal an immediate brake application would result. The release speed is indicated on the speedometer by the illumination of a yellow LED.

If a driver is required to pass a red signal in an emergency, or because the signal has failed, the ATP system can be overridden by pressing a special button, but such action will only be effective if the train is stationary at the signal when the button is pressed. When a driver proceeds past a red signal in such a manner, the train's speed will be controlled to 20mph (32km/h) for 3 minutes, unless it passes over another beacon within that time.

Since the accident at Southall in 1997 (when the ATP system fitted to a train that passed a signal at danger was switched off), the BR-ATP system has been made a permanent installation on the Great Western and Chiltern lines pending future replacement by the European Train Control System (Chapter 26). It has also been installed on the Heathrow Express route and trains. It is not intended to install the BR-ATP system elsewhere, and it is not fitted to all the trains running over the routes fitted with the track equipment.

CHAPTER 25

Ensuring that trains tilt safely

On the West Coast Main Line, tilting trains (Class 390 'Pendolinos' and Class 221 'Super Voyagers') have been authorised to run at speeds above the normal maximum permissible speeds allowed for non-tilting trains, except at large stations and on the *slow lines*. These speeds are referred to as *enhanced permissible speeds* (EPS) and are designated by special lineside speed signs.

Trains must not be allowed to tilt in areas where clearances are tight, or to be driven so fast as to create a risk of derailment or overturning. A new protection system was therefore devised that is known as the *Tilt Authorisation and Supervision System* (TASS).

TASS is based on a simplified version of the European Train Control System (ETCS), and the equipment on the trains (a vital computer operating on a two-out-of-three majority voting system) is installed in the space provided for the ETCS equipment.

Trackside equipment consists of free-standing *Eurobalises,* needing no power supply, located in the 'four-foot' (between the rails) about every 3 miles (5km). They are programmed with information about the speed profile of the route ahead and whether or not the train is authorised to tilt. A tilting train picks up this data as it passes over a balise, and the information is continually updated as the train passes over successive balises.

TASS should be invisible to the driver under normal circumstances and will only intervene to apply the brakes and reduce the speed of the train if the driver exceeds the enhanced permissible speed. Indications on the driver's desk confirm the status of TASS, i.e. that it is 'healthy', the tilt system is authorised and the speed supervised when on a TASS route. They also indicate warnings and interventions to the driver. Should a driver go too fast, an audible warning sounds and the TASS warning/intervention light flashes, advising the driver to reduce speed. If the driver fails to do this, the light shows steady and the brakes are applied to reduce the train's speed to a safe figure. Once having reached a safe speed, the light flashes again and the driver may reset the intervention by pressing the reset button.

ABOVE **A typical TASS balise located in the 'four-foot' of the track on the West Coast Main Line.** *Author*

BELOW LEFT **Enhanced permissible speed sign**

BELOW RIGHT **EPS warning indicator**

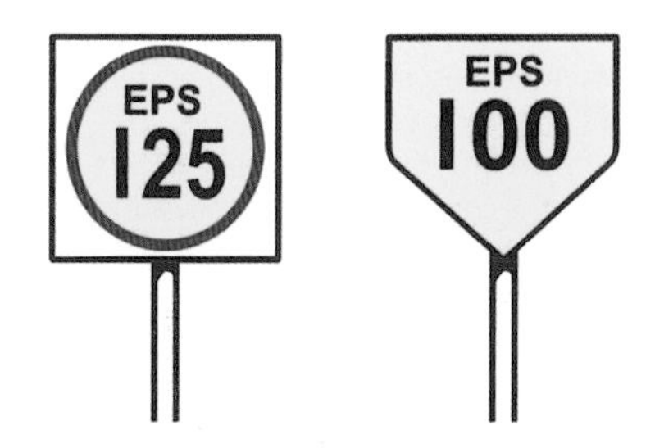

PART 5

CHAPTER 26

The European Rail Traffic Management System (ERTMS)

The European Rail Traffic Management System (ERTMS) has been developed by a consortium of European signalling suppliers in response to directives made by the European Union to facilitate a common signalling system on the designated Trans-European high-speed and conventional rail networks.

The term 'high speed' denotes those lines with speeds of 200km/h (125mph) and above, and in Britain it includes the West Coast and East Coast main lines, the Great Western Main Line and the Channel Tunnel Rail Link, now known as High Speed 1. The conventional network consists of lines with speeds of 160km/h (100mph) and above.

ERTMS has been designed to provide a single standard train control system on those networks to simplify through working from one country to another, through countries and within countries (the term *interoperability* is often used to describe this). Ultimately ERTMS will enable a train passing through many national administration areas to be equipped with ERTMS only. As an example of the present situation, Eurostar trains require five sets of train control equipment.

When existing signalling requires renewal on any of the Trans-European routes, it is a legal requirement that ERTMS is installed. The aim is to avoid all the complications that have arisen from the many different systems of signalling and train control in use at present in the countries of the European Union.

A further advantage of a common train control system is that it enables the European signalling industry to adopt a common specification, which should lead to a cheaper and more reliable product from the various competing signalling equipment manufacturers. ERTMS is defined in what is known as a system requirements specification, maintained by the European Rail Agency, which is updated from time to time as modifications to the system are made.

So far as Britain's railways are concerned, the main benefit is likely to arise from speedier transits of freight across Europe to and from Britain, improving the competitive position of Britain's rail freight companies with respect to road transport. At a domestic level, the main benefits are likely to come from Automatic Train Protection, which is an inherent part of ERTMS, and capacity improvements brought about by the new signalling element of ERTMS, known as the European Train Control System (ETCS). The terms ERTMS and ETCS are often, but wrongly, used interchangeably.

The term 'train control' is a rather comprehensive phrase dating back at least a century to the Great Western Railway's Automatic Train Control, so-called because it could cause the brakes to be applied without any action on the part of the driver. The designers of BR-AWS deliberately avoided using the term 'control' in case it should be interpreted as controlling the speed of the train, both upwards and downwards; it only initiated the braking action. The ATP element of ETCS also initiates the brake action, but train control includes the manner in which instructions are given to the driver, whether by lineside signals or by cab signals or in any other manner. Train control, so far as ETCS is concerned, does not control the driving of the train; that remains with the driver. ETCS only intervenes if the speed is too high, to control the train back to its permitted speed. It does not brake the train to a stand in such circumstances, as would be case following a TPWS intervention.

ETCS has now been fitted to several routes in continental Europe, a process that will continue, with some countries having declared that they will fit their entire networks with ETCS.

In the UK, the railway from Shrewsbury (exclusive) to Aberystwyth and Pwllheli has been fitted with ETCS and is known as the 'Cambrian Early Deployment Scheme'. The purpose of this was to enable experience of ETCS to be gained before any consideration of more widespread fitment to main lines. It has been followed by the

ABOVE Machynlleth station in the ETCS era: Class 158 diesel multiple unit No 158827 arrives with a train to Birmingham New Street on 1 April 2011. *Author*

installation of ETCS on a section of the Hertford Loop line in order to prove different manufacturers' systems, which is known as the 'Hertford National Integration Facility'. The first main line to receive ETCS will be the Great Western Main Line from London to Bristol and South Wales. However, this will be known as an overlay system, because, initially at least, the conventional signalling will remain. The first main line that is likely to migrate totally to ETCS is the East Coast Main Line. The long-term aim is that ETCS will be fitted across the British railway network.

The elements of ERTMS

The four elements of ERTMS are:

1. ETCS covering the signalling interface between the trackside infrastructure and a train
2. GSM-R (Global System for Mobile Communications – Railways), which can be used both for voice communications and for data communications between the part of the system known as the Radio Block Centre (RBC) and trains
3. ETML (European Traffic Management Layer), a concept to optimise railway operations by improved management of train running
4. European Operating Rules, agreed rules to standardise certain aspects of operation across Europe

The Cambrian scheme mentioned above only uses the ETCS and GSM-R elements of ERTMS.

Signalling equipment

The signalling equipment fitted to any ETCS-fitted route extends not only to the track, but also to the trains that run on that route. One of the challenges of ETCS is that not only must the trackside infrastructure be fitted, but all the trains running on the route must also be fitted with ETCS equipment. This can be difficult in the case of older rolling stock, where there may have been no consideration at the design stage that ETCS would later need to be fitted. A considerable number of vehicles may also need to be fitted with the equipment. In the case of the Cambrian scheme, although fitting the ETCS equipment to the Class 158 diesel multiple units was a challenge, only a relatively small number were involved, and these could be made captive to the route.

The three basic parts of the ETCS signalling system are as follows:

1. Conventional signalling equipment such as interlockings, the signaller interface (workstations), train detection (track circuits or axle counters), point machines, ground frame releases, level crossings, and (possibly) lineside signals
2. ETCS trackside equipment such as Radio Block Centres (RBCs), which are responsible for specific sections of railway and provide the communication via GSM-R with ETCS-fitted trains, and Eurobalises (balises), programmed with data that can be 'read' by a passing train, but otherwise are unpowered. There may be more than one balise, which then becomes known as a balise group, and they are used to establish the direction in which a train is going.
3. ETCS train equipment such as the Balise Transmission Module, enabling trains to read the data programmed in balises; odometry equipment to record the position of a train and its speed, typically using two systems; the Traction Interface Unit, which can command the power to be cut off and the brakes to be applied; the Driver Machine Interface in each cab, which provides a visual display for the driver; the Juridical Recording Unit, which continually logs data about the train's journey; and the European Vital Computer, which is the heart of the on-board system, receiving data from and transmitting data to the RBCs and the other on-board equipment.

ETCS levels

ETCS can operate in five different levels, as follows:

ETCS Level 0

Trackside infrastructure that is not fitted with ETCS is known as Level 0.

ETCS Level 1

This is an overlay of ETCS onto the conventional signalling system. Data is stored in balises linked to the signalling system and there is no RBC. The control centre transmits movement authorities, specifying how far and how fast the train can travel, to the on-board computer via the balises. Transmissions to the train are therefore intermittent rather than continuous and enable the computer to calculate updated speed and braking curves each time the train receives the transmitted data. The system provides continuous speed supervision and SPAD protection. Additional balises can be installed on the approach to signals to provide updated information.

ETCS Level 1 provides Automatic Train Protection only. Lineside signals and conventional train detection systems (track circuits and axle counters) continue to be used. In practice, Level 1 is equivalent to the ETCS version of BR-ATP, but there are many technical differences.

ETCS Level 2

Data from and to the RBC is transmitted to and received by the on-board computer continuously, and balises are provided mainly to confirm and update the train's location as it travels along the track. These are self-standing and only powered up as the train passes over them. Lineside signals are not necessary, but the limits of movement authorities issued from the RBC may be marked at the lineside by signs known as block markers. All the information that the driver needs is displayed on the Driver Machine Interface. Conventional train detection systems, such as track circuits or axle counters, and other signalling infrastructure continue to be used. Lineside signals may, however, be retained in certain circumstances, for example to allow trains not equipped with ETCS to use the line concerned, and to provide a fall-back safeguard in case of failure of the radio block centre.

ETCS Level 2 is a fixed block system and is the long-term preferred option for the British railway network, for the benefits of increased line capacity that it allows.

ETCS Level 3

As with Level 2, data from and to the RBC is transmitted to and received by the on-board computer, with balises being provided mainly to confirm the train's location as it travels along the track. The main difference from Level 2 is that lineside signals and other conventional trackside infrastructure are not required. Instead of train detection equipment fitted to the trackside infrastructure, the train itself does the reporting

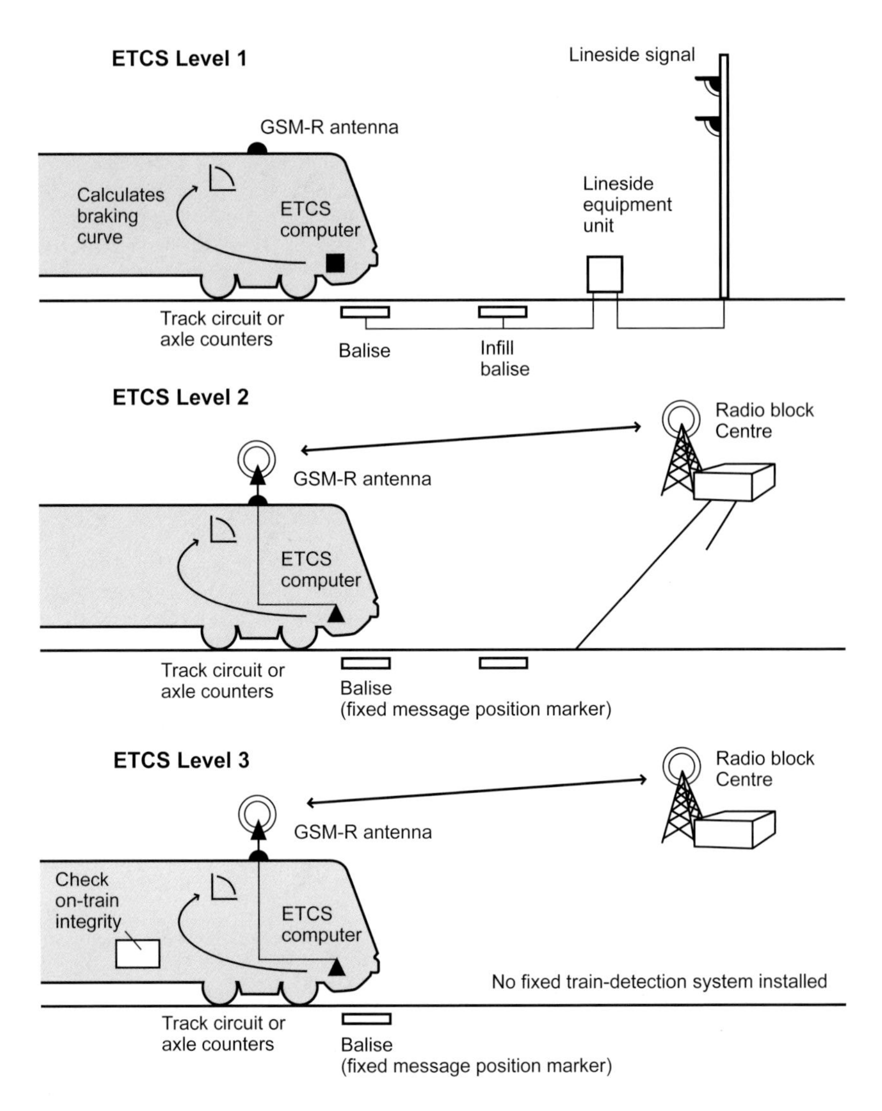

ABOVE The different levels of ETCS

of train position and its integrity (i.e. that the train is complete). Level 3 provides the option of 'moving block' in which trains can, in theory, follow each other at braking distance apart. However, no work is currently being carried out on the development of Level 3 in the UK so this version is unlikely to be available for many years.

ETCS Level Specific Transmission Module (STM)

Level STM allows on-board ETCS equipment to use the data from 'heritage' train protections such as AWS and TPWS and simplifies the transition between different train protection systems.

ETCS Level 2 in practice

The Cambrian Early Deployment Scheme was commissioned in 2011, so a considerable amount of operational experience has now been gained from it. As well as installing the actual equipment on the track and in the trains, the appropriate operational rules had to be drafted and implemented to make the installed ETCS work in practice.

The on-board computer can work in 16 different modes, which include:

1. Full supervision: the normal (default) operating mode in which movement authorities are sent from the RBC to the on-board computer using GSM-R. The Driver Machine Interface (DMI) displays the distance that the train is authorised to travel and its maximum allowed speed. If the train exceeds the maximum speed, the system will shut off power and apply the service brake to reduce the speed.
2. On sight: this mode permits a permissive movement to occur in which there may be another train ahead in the section of line to the end of the signalled move. Speed is supervised to a specific maximum value. The 'distance to go' is displayed to the end of the authority.
3. Shunting: used for unsignalled moves over uncontrolled infrastructure. The on-board computer limits speed to a specific maximum value, and the distance that the train is permitted to travel in this mode may be limited. On the Cambrian scheme, shunt entry boards are provided where required.
4. Staff responsible: used during degraded mode working when there has been a failure of the ETCS equipment. The speed is supervised to a specific maximum limit and the distance that the train can travel in this mode may be limited.

Before a train departs from its origin, the driver has to enter data concerning the train, such as its braking characteristics, into the on-board computer. To simplify this process it is defined in a data set for fixed-formation trains.

As the train progresses along the track, it must receive the correct data to calculate the correct supervision curves. This requires accurate track data (e.g. permissible speeds and gradients) to be sent to the train, and the braking characteristics of the train held by the system to be correct. The train must also keep an accurate record of its position.

Balises, each of which has a unique identity, enable the on-board computer to work out the difference between the balise position on the track and the position as worked out by the on-board odometry (which is likely to be different). It is important that the position of each train is known as accurately as possible so that the appropriate *movement authority* can be issued. These positions will never be known with total accuracy so there is a safety margin built in behind and in front of each train to account for odometry and balise positioning errors.

The signaller's workstation is the same as those in any other modern control centre, and when the signaller (or an ARS system) requests a route from one block marker to another, that request is first sent to the interlocking, which will (if available) set the route and indicate this back to the signaller on the display screen. The RBC will then issue a movement authority to the on-board computer permitting the train to run to a specific point ahead at a specific speed. This information is displayed to the driver on the display panel in the driving cab (the Driver Machine Interface). Before the RBC can issue a movement authority, any points within the route ahead must be set, locked and detected. It will be seen from this that there is a direct analogy between the 'movement authority' and a signal displaying a proceed aspect on a conventionally signalled railway. The movement authority issued by the train must at least contain the following information:

1. The location to which the train is permitted to run
2. The permissible speed profile of the track ahead
3. The gradient profile of the track ahead

The on-board computer supervises the speed of the train to two locations on the track ahead. These are known as the 'end of authority' (marked by a block marker) and the 'supervised location' (this may be likened to the overlap in conventional signalling). The supervised location marks the limit beyond which a train could enter a conflicting section of route, or a level crossing, and can be thought of as the limit of safe overrun distance, or in some cases the overlap. Train speed to the end of authority is supervised by means of a service brake intervention curve, whereby if the train exceeds its permissible speed the system will automatically apply the service brake to reduce the train's speed so that it is able to stop before the end of authority. If the train speed is such that it meets the emergency brake intervention curve, the system will apply the

emergency brake to ensure that, under conditions of normal adhesion, the train stops before reaching the supervised location.

ETCS also incorporates a 'release speed', the purpose of which is to allow a train to approach close to an end of authority, or close to a train ahead standing at the end of authority where permissive working is taking place. Without such a facility, a train would have to stop short of the end of authority, because of margins of error in how the system records train position. This would have implications, for example, in clearing loop points and stopping at the correct point at stations.

The signaller can introduce temporary speed restrictions by keyboard interface, and trains are

ABOVE LEFT The ETCS speedometer and driver's display in the cab of a Class 158 diesel multiple unit. *Author*

LEFT A detailed view of an ETCS speedometer showing that the train is currently running at 68km/h with a target speed of 80km/h. *RAIB*

BELOW In this example, the Driver Machine Interface speedometer is showing 39km/h and the maximum speed (the speed hook) is showing 98km/h.

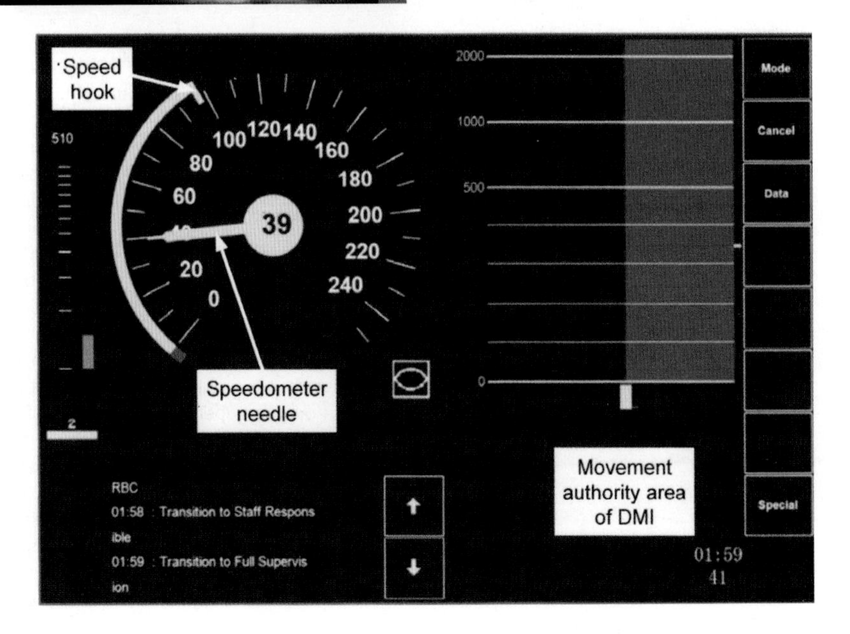

ABOVE ETCS track-mounted balises at Harlech station provided to update positional information relating to a train. *Author*

ABOVE A signaller's workstation in the control centre at Machynlleth. *Author*

BELOW A detailed view of one of the signaller's display screens showing the Machynlleth station area, with train 1J11 (indicated by the solid red line) in the up platform. The lineside block markers are denoted on the screen by the solid red triangles. *Author*

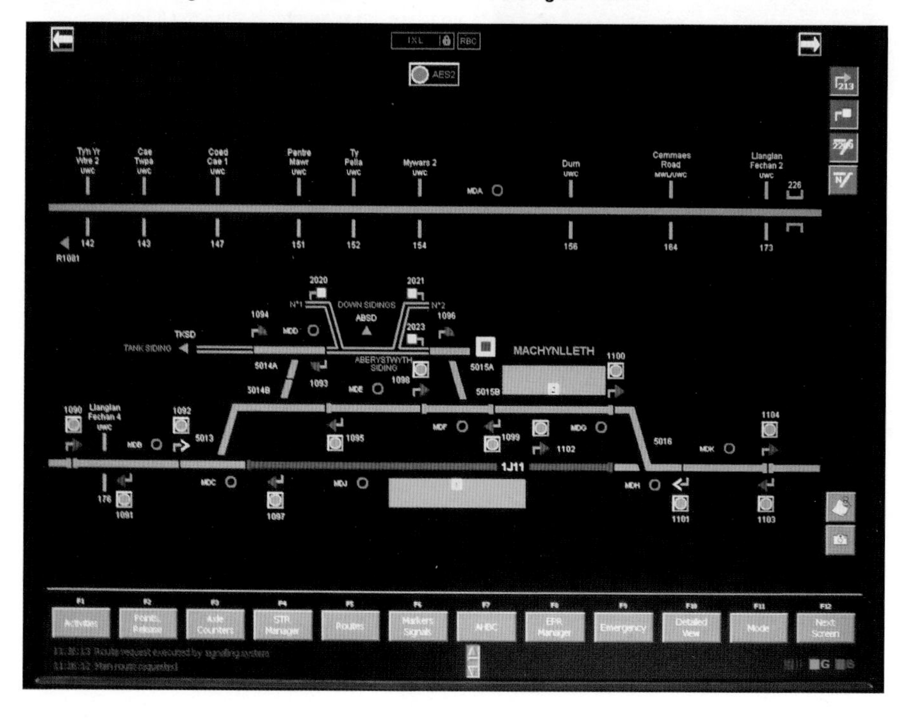

then supervised to ensure that they comply with the speed restriction.

SPADs can still occur if the train exceeds the end of authority because the driver did not apply the brake in time during a normal approach. The end of authority can also be exceeded following receipt of a release speed. In both cases, the system should prevent the train from going beyond the danger point, and it should therefore be protected.

The performance benefits of ETCS

The performance benefits of Level 2 ETCS include:

1. The train and its driver can 'see' further along the route ahead, enabling more efficient driving.
2. Signal spacing, which has to be set for the trains with the worst braking characteristics on a route, is no longer a constraint in freeing up line capacity.
3. Temporary speed restrictions can be configured and implemented in real time, much more quickly than with conventional equipment.
4. There are fewer physical assets so there is less opportunity for failure and less equipment to maintain. The system should be more reliable.
5. Bi-directional running is much easier to build into the system and implement when required. ETCS should result in many more routes having bi-directional running.
6. A higher speed approach into already occupied platforms is possible when permissive working is in force.
7. Faster approaches to diverging junctions are also possible; ETCS will ensure that speed is controlled to an appropriate level for a diverging, lower-speed movement. This will invariably be a lot less restrictive than the current approach release of the junction signal arrangement.
8. The time taken to set up and remove possessions taken for engineering work should be substantially reduced.

ABOVE ETCS block marker MH1235 at Harlech station, showing the physical limit of an issued movement authority. The other signage present applies to the level crossing immediately ahead, with the St George's cross applying to a further crossing beyond. *Author*

PART 6

CHAPTER 27

Signalling on High Speed 1

The signalling system installed on the new line from St Pancras International to and through the Channel Tunnel, and on to Paris on the TGV Nord high-speed line, is a slightly adapted version of a French system known as *TVM430* (except in the St Pancras International station area). There are no lineside signals, and the driver is informed of the speed at which the train is to travel, or whether it is required to stop, by the display of information in the driving cab. Automatic Train Protection is an inherent part of the system.

The St Pancras International station area served by High Speed 1 is signalled with lineside colour light signals, and the French KVB (*Contrôle Vitesse par Balise*) system of Automatic Train Protection has been fitted (note that the platforms used by domestic services to the East Midlands and the North are fitted with conventional British signalling). The KVB system is fitted as standard throughout the French railway system, including on the approaches to Paris Gare du Nord. Trains on High Speed 1 therefore have to switch from cab signalling under the TVM430 system to lineside signals with KVB as they approach St Pancras International station.

Track equipment

TVM430 lines are track-circuited throughout and are divided into 1,500-metre block sections with, at the end of each block, a marker board consisting of a metal plate painted blue with a yellow horizontal triangle to provide a reference point for the driver. These are of two types: 'non-passable' and 'passable'. When closed (the equivalent to being at danger), non-passable markers can only be passed on the authority of the signaller, and each is also fitted with an auxiliary signal consisting of two lights, similar to a position light signal. These flash white when the signaller has set a route (an auxiliary route) during abnormal working such as a track circuit failure ahead. Passable markers are not fitted with the auxiliary signal, and can be passed when closed without the authority of the signaller provided that the train speed does not exceed 35km/h. Information is transmitted to the train by means of coded track circuits via the running rails.

The lineside signals at St Pancras are of the fibre-optic type and have halogen lamps for both the main and auxiliary aspects in either the base of the signal or in a separate cabinet. The light is fed to the signal head by means of fibre-

LEFT A Eurostar train emerges from the southern portal of the North Downs Tunnel on High Speed 1. *Author*

ABOVE A 'passable' block marker on High Speed 1 with, lower down the post, a local 'Engineering Zone of Protection' switch. *Author*

ABOVE A 'non-passable' block marker, with an auxiliary signal below. *Author*

optic cables. The posts have been designed to tilt to the ground so that maintenance (such as cleaning the lenses) can be carried out from ground level, avoiding the need for ladders or other access equipment.

Train equipment

Trains are fitted with antennae that receive coded data, transmitted by audio-frequency track circuits, containing information about the state of the line ahead. An on-board computer calculates the maximum speed at which the train may travel, including a braking curve if a reduction of speed is necessary. The driver controls the speed of the train, but if it exceeds the maximum permitted speed on the cab display, or strays outside the braking curve, the brakes will be applied.

The speed codes received by the train contain information about the current maximum safe speed in the block, the target speed at the end of the block, and the target speed at the end of the next block. These can each be of five different values corresponding to a typical deceleration curve (300, 270, 230, 170 and 0km/h).

Train controls

The signalling control system is based on the maintenance of a number of unoccupied 1,500-metre blocks in front of a train. Braking from 300km/h requires five blocks, and an additional 'buffer' block is provided in case of accidental overrun. At this speed, trains are typically about 10.5km apart, or about 3 minutes' running time.

High Speed 1 is controlled from Ashford control centre, and the Channel Tunnel from the control centre in France at Coquelles, or Folkestone. Either of these can take over control of the tunnel if the other was to be out of action for any reason. Automatic route setting is employed on a large scale.

Out-of-course working

Temporary speed restrictions can be imposed through the TVM430 system, either by the signaller, or by maintenance staff using lockable switches in signalling equipment rooms. Speed restriction bands are limited to 80, 170, 220 and 270km/h. Speed restrictions can also be imposed using speed boards and portable KVB beacons.

Engineering possessions are taken by the operation of *engineering zones of protection* (EZP) by the signaller at Ashford control centre. This prevents routes, other than auxiliary routes, into the protected area from being set. Local switches are also operated by the responsible person on site. If the possession is of one line only, a speed restriction is imposed by the system on the adjacent line.

Detonators and track circuit operating devices are not used on High Speed 1.

PART 7

CHAPTER 28

Working of single lines

Introduction

The fundamental difference between the working of double lines and single lines is that on single lines, where trains run in both directions, there must be protection against trains travelling in opposite directions colliding, as well as protection against rear-end collisions. This is easily achieved on lines signalled under the track circuit block principle where, if the whole line is signalled by one control centre, no additional measures are required over and above those provided by a normal interlocking. Put simply, the signals at each end of a single line section for opposite-direction movements are interlocked with one another, and this interlocking is maintained until the train has passed through the section and is clear of the single line at the other end. Such arrangements may apply not only to the single-track railway from one place to another, but also to track layouts where some or all lines are signalled for movements in both directions, known as bi-directional lines. In other places double-track railways are provided with signalling in simplified form to permit train movements in the wrong direction; these enable, for example, one line to be blocked for engineering work, or so that a failed train can be passed. No special provisions are required either on lines signalled with ETCS.

If the signals cannot be interlocked in the way described above, the train must carry a unique token as its authority to enter the single-line section.

Several methods of single line signalling are in use for lines not provided with continuous train detection and modern signalling, as described below.

The electric token block system

The *electric token block* system was devised to guarantee safety by ensuring that every train passing through a single-line section carries a token obtained from a *token instrument*, of which there is one at each end of each section. The instruments at each end of a section are electrically interlocked so that it is only possible for one token to be 'out' (i.e. in use) for the section at one time. The token may take the form of a circular tablet, several centimetres in diameter, or a metal key about 150mm (6 inches) long. It is placed in a leather pouch with a large loop handle to facilitate the handover from signaller to driver while on the move, and vice versa. The token is able to be withdrawn from the token instrument when the correct bell signals have been exchanged and all the relevant stop and distant signals are in the danger position. When the train has passed through the section the token is inserted in the instrument at the other end, and

LEFT Electric key token instruments showing the entry point for each token underneath the needle and the storage slots for tokens covering the section controlled. *Stuart Johnson*

the 'train out of section' bell signal is sent. Each instrument can contain around 30 tokens.

At a crossing loop on a single line, a train may only be accepted from the adjacent signal box if the loop line for which the facing points are set and on which the train will run is clear to the loop exit signal. When trains are approaching a crossing place from opposite directions, the home signals in both directions must be kept at danger, until the train that is to enter the loop first has stopped, after which the home signal may be cleared to allow it to draw forward. When it has stopped again in the loop the home signal may be cleared for the other train to enter the loop on the other side.

Tokenless block systems

These systems depend on drivers correctly observing and responding to signals, but there is no token. There is therefore no need for the train to slow down to collect the token, which is a major operating inconvenience if the train is not stopping anyway. A continuous system of train detection is not required and safe operation is maintained by the release of the starting signal through the operation of block instruments.

In the British Railways *tokenless block* system, safety is provided by the sequential occupation and clearance of track circuits at both signal boxes, so that the signals cannot be cleared for a second train to enter the section from either direction until the previous train is proved to have passed through the section. Although block instruments are required, there are no block bells. The instruments have a three-position needle indicator; an acceptance switch with two positions, either 'Normal' or 'Accept'; and two plungers for 'Offer' and 'Train arrived'.

The method of signalling is as follows:

1. Trains are accepted by placing the acceptance switch in the 'Accept' position. This is the usual position, depending on the anticipated movement of trains.
2. Before the dispatch of a train, the signaller must press the 'Offer' button, provided that the block indicator and the acceptance switch for that section are at 'Normal'. If the acceptance switch at the signal box ahead is at 'Accept', the needle indicators in both signal boxes will move to 'Train accepted', and the signaller at the start of the section may then clear the section signal and tell the other signaller the description of the train. When the train occupies the track circuit ahead of the section signal, the needle indicator will move to 'Train in section'. After the train has passed through the section, it registers its arrival by operating a treadle at the home signal; and after it has occupied and cleared the track circuit ahead of the home signal at the end of the section, the signaller there must place the acceptance switch to 'Normal'.

   When the train, complete with tail lamp, arrives, the signaller must operate the 'Train arrived' button, which will restore the block indicators to 'Normal'. The acceptance switch must be maintained at 'Normal' until the train has passed the clearing point.

The above description is of the system fitted to the railway from Salisbury to Exeter when it was taken over by the Western Region (WR) and much of it was singled (this tokenless block equipment has now itself been replaced following resignalling of the line, but WR tokenless block is still in use in a few other places). The Scottish Region developed its own system and fitted it to most of the Highland Line, between Perth and Inverness (although sections of that route have now been fitted with different signalling), and to other lines, including that between Aberdeen and Inverness. It is designed to be as much like the electric key token system as possible but without the physical token. Communication between signal boxes is by the use of normal block bells. A further variation of the tokenless block system is *direction lever tokenless block*, in which the opposite-direction signals are interlocked by a direction lever in the signal box at the end of the section. Once a train has entered the section, the position of the direction lever cannot be changed until the train is detected as having cleared the section.

The 'no-signaller' token with remote crossing loops (NSTR) system

The NSTR system is used mainly on quiet rural lines, such as the Central Wales Line from Craven Arms to Pantyffynon, where each passing loop is fitted with point indicators and stop boards and the whole

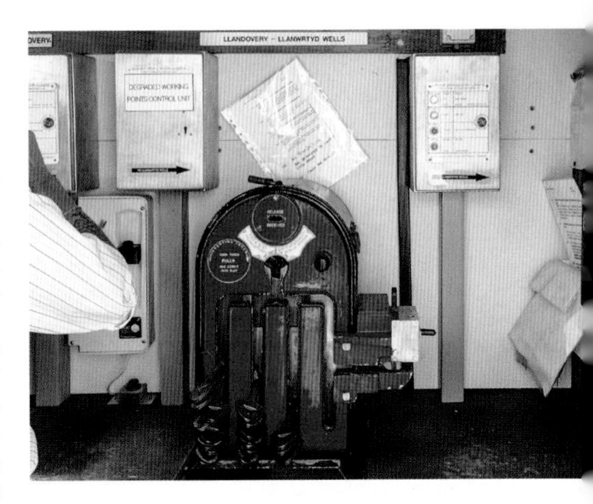

RIGHT The NSTR token instrument at Llandovery covering the section of line to Llanwrtyd Wells. *RAIB*

route can come under the supervision of one signal box. The system is similar in principle to electric key token, and the trackside infrastructure of signals and signage is very similar to the Radio Electronic Token Block system described below. The NSTR system has a token instrument for each single-line section, so a passing loop has two token instruments, one for the driver to surrender the token for the single-line section just traversed, and the second for the driver to remove a token for the following section. However, before being able to do so, the driver must call the signaller and obtain the signaller's authority. Once the driver has the correct token, the train can pass the stop board. The Train Protection and Warning System (TPWS) is fitted to stop boards so that if a train departs without the correct token, the brakes will be applied to stop the train.

The Radio Electronic Token Block system (RETB)

This system was born of the need to reduce the costs of working the long single lines to be found in Northern Scotland, Central Wales and elsewhere, in order to avoid having to close them down. It requires no intermediate signal boxes or signallers, nor does it require a vulnerable telegraph pole route, because all messages are sent by radio. It is based in theory on the well-tried and reliable electric token block system, but the 'token' is passed between signaller and driver electronically by radio, instead of physically by hand. The lineside infrastructure is very similar to lines signalled using the NSTR system.

The whole line is controlled by one signaller, who has an operating console containing a representation of the track under the control of the signalling centre, together with electronic equipment and computers ensuring that tokens are only issued for sections of line when it is safe to do so. Each driver's cab is equipped with radio and an RETB instrument containing two windows in which the electronic token displays its presence by showing the two ends of the section through which the train is authorised to travel.

To enter a single-line section, the driver must radio the signaller for permission. If the previous train in the same direction has passed through the section and cleared the next crossing loop, and if no train has been authorised to proceed through the section from the other end, the signaller issues an electronic token to the driver. To enable this to take place, both the driver and the signaller must simultaneously press a button on their equipment (known as a '*handshake*'). The driver will then confirm that the token has been received, because it will have appeared on the RETB instrument in the cab, and the signaller will verbally authorise the driver to proceed (this takes the place of the section signal). On entering the single-line section the driver reports to the signaller by radio as soon as the train has cleared the loop. This is important for two reasons: first, because as soon as the loop is clear another train travelling in the same direction can be allowed to leave the previous loop, and second, if for any reason the driver had left the loop and entered the single-line section without authority (potentially very dangerous, and a risk that should now be protected by TPWS – see below), the signaller would become aware of it and tell the driver to stop at once. The signaller would also issue a similar instruction to the driver of any train coming through the single-line section in the opposite direction.

In order to keep costs down, the points at loops are not normally worked by the signaller (who is likely to be many miles away). They were originally hydro-pneumatically operated so that they always lay towards the same loop line and were capable of being trailed through from the

ABOVE On the West Highland Line, where trains are controlled using the RETB system, Class 156 No 156492 waits at Glenfinnan with a Mallaig service on 13 July 2008. *Author*

BELOW A typical single-track branch line with passing loops worked under the RETB system

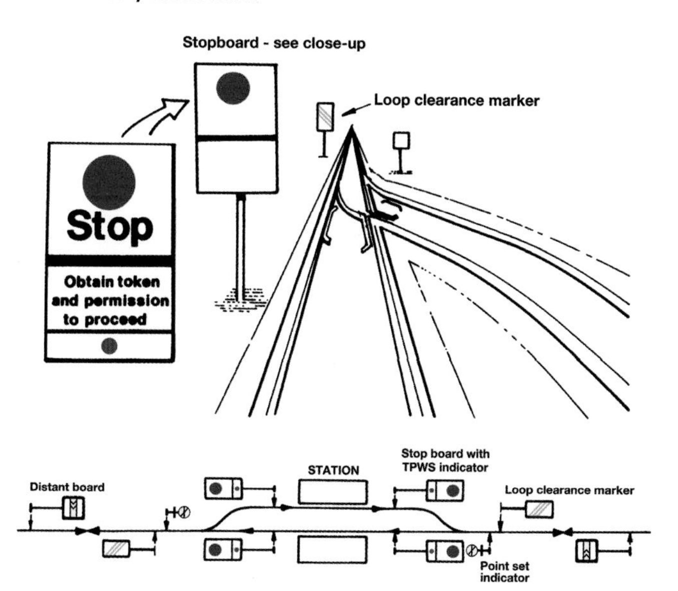

ABOVE The RETB signage at the west end of Glenfinnan station. Of note are the TPWS train stop sensor grids and the TPWS blue signals under each stop board. These flash when the TPWS is suppressed, allowing a train to depart without receiving a TPWS intervention. *Author*

BELOW The sequence of indicators and boards at a crossing loop on a single line worked under the RETB system

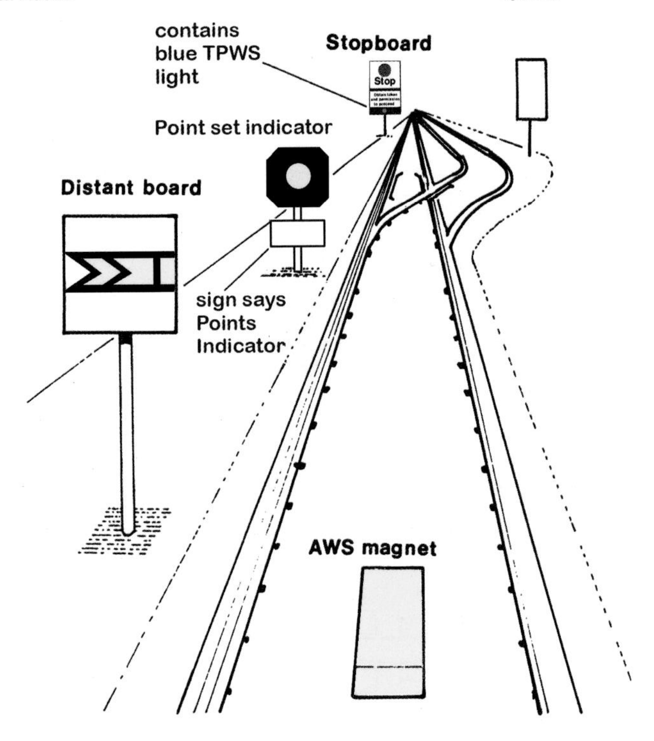

other loop line. In recent years, some of these points have been converted to conventional operation, with electric point machines operated, detected and locked by radio command.

When a train has entered a loop and is clear of the single-line section, the driver informs the signaller accordingly by radio. Both will press the appropriate buttons on their equipment simultaneously, and the electronic token will be returned to the signaller. The driver's RETB instrument display will clear, and the token will appear on the signaller's console display. If the section ahead is clear, the procedure for the issue of an electronic token for that section may then take place to enable the driver to proceed.

The signal box computer ensures that tokens are issued in the correct sequence, keeps a record of all trains on the line, and prevents the signaller from authorising conflicting train movements.

Transponders located in the track can detect the position of the train and announce it by radio to the signaller.

TPWS has been fitted to lines equipped with the RETB system, necessitating the provision of special equipment to suppress the train stop sensors when an electronic token has been issued. This in turn necessitated the development of an indicator to advise drivers when the TPWS is suppressed, which consists of a blue light. When the TPWS is active, the indicator shows steady, but when it is suppressed the indicator flashes.

Dead-end branch lines

One train working is in use on some dead-end branch lines where the train service is sufficiently infrequent that it does not require more than one train to be on the branch at once. There are two methods. In one a token known as a *train staff* is provided and a train must not enter the branch line unless the driver is in possession of it. In the other, there is no train staff, and the clearance of the controlling signal is the only authority for the train to enter the branch. Safety in the latter case is achieved by the occupation and clearance of a track circuit, located at the entrance to the branch, on two occasions (i.e. when the train enters and when it returns). The controlling signal cannot be cleared for a second train until the first one is proved to have returned by the operation of the track circuits.

A train staff is provided at those locations where there is someone, usually a signaller, who can act as its custodian and hand it over to the driver when required. The other method – the tokenless method – is mainly used on lines controlled from a remote signal box, such as a power signal box, where there is no one available at or near the branch entrance to look after the train staff.

In the *no signaller key token system* (NSKT), one train can follow another along the branch line as soon as the first is proved to have arrived at the far end of the branch. This is achieved by the use of tokens, and there is a token instrument at each end of the branch line. The token instrument at the junction of the main line and the branch is operated by the signaller, who issues a token to a driver in the usual way, allowing the train to proceed on to the branch line (or in some cases, gives a release from a remote signalling centre to enable the driver to extract a token from the machine), provided that no other token is 'out'. When the train arrives at the far end of the branch, and is clear of an 'End of Single Line Section' notice board, the driver places the token in an instrument there, thus allowing another train to use the branch line, either by following the first train or by setting off in the opposite direction. It avoids the cost of having a signal box and signaller at the end of the branch. The signaller controls the issue of tokens from the machine at the far end, by the use of a release.

Failures of equipment

With all these systems, provision must be made for train movements to continue safely, albeit at reduced speed, when the signalling equipment controlling the tokens is faulty, or a token is lost or damaged, or track circuits have failed. It is vital to ensure that only one train is in the single-line section at once, and this is done by introducing a system known as working by *pilotman*. In this system a person is appointed pilotman, and is responsible for the safety of the single line. The pilotman must personally authorise drivers to proceed and must travel through the single-line section with the driver when the next train requiring to pass through it will do so from the other end. On 'one train working' sections the pilotman must travel with every train.

CHAPTER 29

Manually operated level crossings with gates or barriers

Level crossings are of considerable concern to the railway industry, representing as they do the interface between the highly disciplined and regulated railway and the much less disciplined and regulated highway. There are several different types of crossing as described in the following text, but broadly the railway industry classifies them as follows:

1. Active crossings – where the road vehicle or pedestrian is warned of the approach of the train through the closure of gates or barriers and/or by warning (i.e. stop) lights or alarms.
2. Passive crossings – where no warning of a train is given other than by the train driver, who might use the train horn. The onus is on the road user or pedestrian to determine whether or not it is safe to cross the line.

ABOVE A typical automatic half barrier level crossing. This is at Grives Lane, Sutton-in-Ashfield, with a northbound Robin Hood Line service from Nottingham about the pass over the crossing. *Author*

RIGHT A user-worked crossing with the usual outward-opening gates. This one is protected with miniature stop lights, which change to red when it is unsafe to cross. *Author*

They can also be classified as:

1. Public crossings
   a. Vehicular, which must be manually or automatically operated. Modernised vehicle crossings that are changed from the original gates to a newer form of protection, or subsequently upgraded again to a different system, must be authorised by a statutory order issued by the statutory regulator, the Office of Rail and Road.
   b. Bridleway or footpath crossings open to the public, with the onus on the crossing user to ensure their own safety.
2. Private ('user-worked') crossings, which are usually vehicular crossings, and are of two types:
   a. Occupation: where a private access road is crossed by the railway
   b. Accommodation: where the land is split in two by the railway
   In both types, crossing users have a duty to shut the gates across the roadway following use.

The accompanying table lists the various types of manually controlled public level crossing, together with the number of each type in use, on Network Rail as of May 2016:

MANUALLY CONTROLLED PUBLIC LEVEL CROSSINGS	
Gates controlled by a signaller on site	149
Barriers controlled by a signaller or other operator on site	173
Barriers controlled remotely by a signaller or other operator and supervised by CCTV	422
Barriers controlled through a system of obstacle detection supervised by a signaller or other operator	81

Level crossing gates and barriers are not considered to be an obstruction so far as the acceptance of trains by a signaller is concerned (under the absolute block, tokenless block or key token block regulations).

Gates controlled by a signaller on site

The gates swing alternately across the road and the railway. Legally, they are required to be normally closed across the road, but the Office of Rail and Road may authorise the gates at any particular level crossing to be normally closed across the railway, and this has been done at most level crossings because of the frequency of road traffic. The gates are interlocked with the railway signals in such a way that the signals cannot be cleared unless the gates are across the road. Once the signals have been cleared, the gates cannot then be moved back across the railway.

Where road traffic is heavy, and the signaller finds it difficult to swing the gates across the road because there are insufficient gaps in the traffic, road traffic light signals may be provided, which the signaller can switch to red to enable him to swing his gates. The gates often used to be operated by a large wheel in the signal box, but in most cases are now pushed across by hand.

Gates controlled by a crossing keeper on site

These gates are usually to be found in rural areas where neither road nor rail traffic is heavy. For historical reasons they are of many types. A crossing keeper who lives in a cottage at the crossing may operate them, or they may be operated by non-resident crossing keepers, working shifts, or by a combination of both, depending on the flow of road and rail traffic.

The gates may be of the signal box type alternately closing the road and the railway, or they may be field gates, which open away from the railway. The gates are normally pushed across by hand.

Protecting railway signals are provided at some, but not all, crossings of this type. In some cases both distant and stop signals are provided (normally semaphore); in other cases only distant signals are provided. Sometimes the signals are interlocked with the gates, and sometimes they are not.

There are various methods of informing crossing keepers as to whether they may open the gates to allow road traffic to cross. At some crossings duplicate block indicators are provided. Duplicate bells may also be provided. At other crossings the crossing keeper has to telephone a nearby signal box to ask the signaller if road traffic may be allowed across.

LEFT At the former gated crossing at Attleborough, between Ely and Norwich, the signaller was required to push the gates across by hand. This crossing has since been modernised and is now a manually controlled barrier crossing with obstacle detection. *RAIB*

Barriers controlled by a signaller or other operator on site

Barriers controlled by a signaller or other operator on site are known as *manually controlled crossings* or MCBs. Lifting barriers are normally installed as a modern replacement for gates, and are operated electrically. The barriers close the full width of the road at each side of the level crossing when lowered, but are normally kept in the raised position. They are interlocked with the protecting railway signals and there are usually road traffic light signals too.

To lower the barriers the operator will press a button marked 'Lower' on the control console. The amber light on the road traffic signals shows for about 3 seconds, after which the red lights start to flash. After 4 to 6 seconds, the *nearside* barriers start to descend, and when they are fully lowered, the offside barriers descend. Before the railway signals can be cleared, the crossing operator must check that the crossing is clear (i.e. that no vehicle or person is trapped on the crossing between the lowered barriers) and press a 'Crossing clear' button. Both the barrier lowering and raising sequences can be initiated automatically by trains through the operation of track circuits, but it is still be necessary for the operator to check that the crossing is clear, and press the 'Crossing clear' button, before the railway signals can be cleared. After the train has passed, all the barriers rise simultaneously.

On narrow roads it is usual to provide only one lifting barrier on each side of the railway to fully close off the road when lowered.

Approach locking is provided to ensure that once the barriers have been lowered and the signals cleared, the barriers cannot be raised again in error. In the event of a protecting signal being put back to danger when an approaching train is too close to be able to stop at it, the approach locking will lock the barriers in the down position until the train has either passed over the crossing, or has stopped before it.

Barriers controlled remotely by a signaller or other operator and supervised by CCTV

The barrier equipment and method of control are very similar to the MCB crossing described above, the only difference being that instead of the signaller checking visually that the crossing is clear, it is done by means of a *closed circuit television* (CCTV) camera mounted at the level crossing, which relays a picture to a monitor in the signal box. Audible and visual indications are provided at the signal box to show if the main power supply fails, or if a barrier is dislodged (e.g. by high wind, or a road vehicle running into it).

CCTV installations enable a signaller to control level crossings remote from the signal box and enable several to be controlled from the same location. CCTV operation is widely used in power signal box areas. The signalling controls

RIGHT The manually controlled barrier crossing at Sutton Junction, Nottinghamshire, is controlled using CCTV from the East Midlands Control Centre in Derby. *Author*

LEFT The monitor for Clay Mills manually controlled barrier crossing, just north of Burton-on-Trent, in the East Midlands Control Centre. This shows the barriers lowering, following which the signaller will check the crossing is unobstructed before pressing the 'Crossing clear' button. *Author*

ABOVE The control panel for Clay Mills manually controlled barrier crossing, showing the 'Lower', 'Raise' and 'Crossing clear' buttons. *Author*

are as for the MCB type of crossing described above, with the railway signals being interlocked with the barriers.

Barriers controlled through a system of obstacle detection supervised by a signaller or other operator

This is a recent development of the manually controlled barrier crossing in which the 'Crossing clear' function is carried out by a system of obstacle detection. This reduces the workload of the signaller, who does not need to intervene in the working of the crossing. It was developed following the accident at Ufton Nervet *automatic half barrier crossing* in November 2004 in which a car driver parked a car on the crossing, which was subsequently struck by a train.

Two systems of obstacle detection are required: a radar system that scans most of the crossing between the lowered barriers, and a laser scanning system that scans the extremities of the crossing outside the area covered by the radar system.

This type of crossing works effectively as an automatic full barrier crossing in which the barriers are lowered by an approaching train; the

ABOVE Traffic waits at the manually controlled barrier crossing at Wellowgate, Grimsby, as the 13.49 service from Grimsby to Newark North Gate passes over it on 2 February 2016. This crossing has obstacle detection to confirm that the crossing is clear before any railway signals on the approach may be cleared. *Author*

ABOVE The obstacle detection equipment at Wellowgate level crossing, Grimsby. Nearest the camera can be seen the radar detector, then adjacent to it and between the tracks is the laser detection system that covers areas of the crossing not covered by the radar system. *Author*

obstacle detection system then confirms that the crossing is clear and permits the protecting signals on the approach to be cleared; and finally the barriers are raised by the passage of the train as it leaves the crossing. CCTV supervision is not required, but video recording is installed to provide a record of any incidents that occur.

CHAPTER 30

Automatic level crossings

The accompanying table lists the various types of automatic level crossing, together with the number of each type in use on Network Rail as of May 2016.

Automatic half barrier crossings (AHBs)
Automatic half barrier crossings, first introduced on British Railways in 1961, have three objectives:

AUTOMATIC LEVEL CROSSINGS	
Automatic half barrier crossings (AHB)	437
Automatic barrier crossings, locally monitored (ABCL)	57
Automatic open crossings, locally monitored with barrier (AOCL-B)	66
Automatic open crossings, locally or remotely monitored (AOCL/R)	31
Many ABCLs were converted from the now obsolete automatic open crossings, remotely monitored (AOCR), of which only one remains, at Rosarie, between Keith and Elgin. The 63 AOCL-Bs are upgrades of the original AOCLs in which half barriers have been fitted retrospectively to improve safety.	

1. To avoid the staffing costs of ordinary level crossings
2. To reduce the delays to road traffic caused by conventional gated or manually controlled barrier level crossings
3. To improve safety at level crossings, by eliminating errors by railway staff during normal operation

So far as these three objectives are concerned, AHBs have only been introduced where the saving in staff costs more than outweighs their costs. They considerably reduce delays to road traffic because they are not generally interlocked with railway signals, so that the crossing does not need to be closed to road traffic for a long period.

The barriers, extending over half the carriageway on each side, are operated ('struck in') by an approaching train occupying a track circuit, supplemented by duplicated treadles at the running-on end (i.e. the end remote from the crossing) to guard against unreliable operation of the track circuit by lightweight vehicles.

AHBs are designed so that the warning to road users is a minimum of 27 seconds from the amber lights first showing until a train arrives at the

RIGHT The automatic half barrier crossing at Newstead on the Robin Hood Line from Nottingham to Mansfield. *Author*

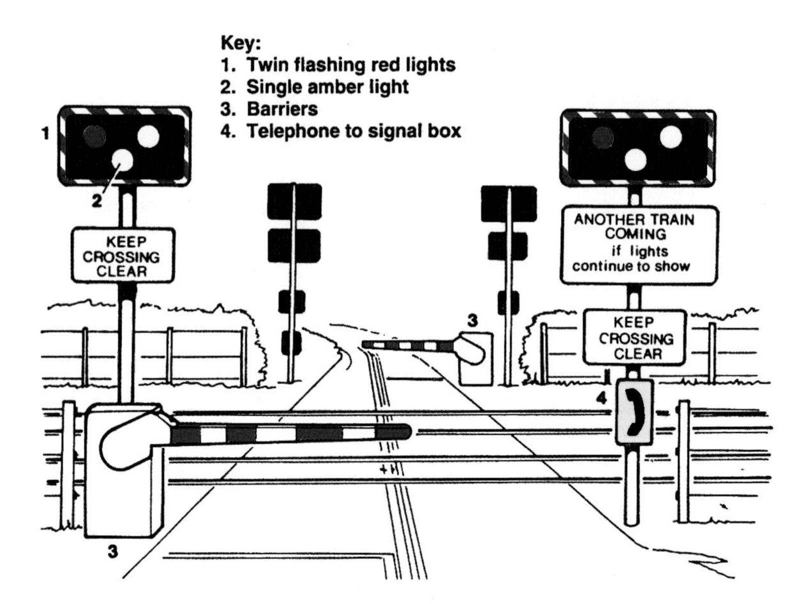

ABOVE An automatic half barrier level crossing, showing the layout, road traffic signals, etc.

crossing. Unless predictor technology is installed to provide a constant warning time for road users, irrespective of the speed of approaching trains, this time may be significantly longer for slower trains. This is undesirable as it increases the risk of careless or reckless motorists ignoring the red flashing lights and deliberately zigzagging around the barriers, occasionally at the cost of their lives. The standard requirements are that 50% of trains on the route should arrive at the crossing within 50 seconds, and 95% within 75 seconds.

At a manually controlled crossing, the road has to be closed and the railway signals cleared before the driver of an approaching train has come within sight of the first caution signal. This can lead to the road being closed to road traffic for several minutes, but because the barriers extend across the whole road, the possibility of vehicles zigzagging round the barriers is eliminated. AHBs do not have full barriers because there must always be an exit route for any vehicle on the crossing after the barriers come down.

At AHBs the railway signals generally act independently of the operation of the level crossing; the nearest railway signals may be green while road traffic is passing over the crossing. The exception to this is where there is a stop signal located close to the crossing within the track circuit that operates the crossing sequence. If a train approaches such a signal at danger, the crossing will not 'strike in' as normal, but will remain open to road traffic until the signal is ready to clear. The clearance of the signal may then be delayed to ensure that the train will not start and reach the crossing in less than 27 seconds from the amber lights showing. Such signals are known as regulating signals.

Complications also arise when there is a station within the track circuit that operates the crossing sequence. Special stopping/non-stopping controls are normally provided, operated by the signaller, so that for a stopping train the crossing does not strike in until the train is ready to depart from the station. A starting signal will have been specially provided, the clearance of which will be delayed to ensure that the minimum 27 seconds time is not infringed. For a non-stopping train, the signal works normally.

AHBs operate according to the following sequence of events:

1. An amber light in each road traffic light shows for 3 seconds.

2. Twin red lights ('wig-wags') commence to flash alternately.
3. After 4-6 seconds the barriers start to lower. The barrier-lowering operation takes between 6 and 10 seconds.
4. Not less than 27 seconds after the amber lights first show, the train arrives at the crossing.
5. The barriers rise as soon as the train has cleared the crossing, unless another train is approaching, in which case they remain down unless at least 10 seconds can elapse after the barriers have begun to rise before the operating cycle recommences for the second train.
6. An audible warning to pedestrians sounds during the whole of the period from the first showing of the amber light to the extinguishing of the red lights. The frequency of the warning sound increases if a second train is coming.

The equipment at the crossing is monitored from a control point (usually a signal box) and emergency telephones are provided to enable the public to speak to the control point.

AHBs may only be provided where the following conditions apply:

1. The maximum speed of trains does not exceed 100mph (160km/h).
2. There are no more than two running lines.
3. The road on the approaches to the crossing must be wide enough to enable vehicles to pass safely so that they do not block the crossing.
4. There must be no bumps or hollows in the road that might cause a low vehicle to ground on the crossing (known as the *vertical profile*).
5. The road layout (e.g. nearby junctions) and traffic conditions (e.g. frequency of hold-ups) must be such that there is no significant risk of road vehicles blocking the crossing and obstructing the railway.

Equipment is provided at the level crossing to allow the lights and barriers to be locally controlled on site in circumstances such as:

1. Failure of equipment
2. Repairs to the equipment
3. Work on the track
4. Roadworks near the crossing that might cause traffic to block back

When the crossing is being controlled locally, the signaller must warn the driver of each train to approach the crossing cautiously and not pass over it unless authorised by a green flag or lamp being displayed by the attendant.

Some AHB crossings are adapted to allow wrong-direction movements to operate the lights and barriers in the normal way. They are designated as AHB-X level crossings, and the train speed must not exceed that shown on the wrong direction speed restriction board, which has black numerals prefixed by the letter X on a white background, normally positioned on the right-hand side of the line.

ABOVE A speed restriction board for trains approaching an AHB level crossing in the wrong direction

The operational status of the crossing is indicated at the supervising control point. Should the crossing fail, the signaller must arrange for an attendant to operate the crossing locally if possible, and caution approaching trains by stopping them at the closest stop signal and instructing their drivers to proceed at slow speed over the crossing. If the road lights are flashing, they must continue to be observed by road traffic. Even emergency services vehicles are not permitted to pass the flashing red lights at a level crossing.

Automatic locally monitored crossings

These are of three types:

1. Automatic barrier crossings, locally monitored (ABCL)
2. Automatic open crossings, locally monitored (AOCL)
3. Automatic open crossings, locally monitored with barrier (AOCL-B) (as AOCL above, but retrofitted with half barriers)

LEFT The locally monitored automatic open crossing at Launton between Bicester and Calvert, part of the former cross-country route from Oxford to Cambridge. Currently freight-only, it is planned to reopen this line to passenger trains as part of the East West Rail initiative. *Author*

These types of crossing have been installed where the nature of the train service allows speeds to be reduced on the approach to the crossing to a level at which the train driver can check (a) that the road traffic signals are flashing (and the barriers at ABCLs are lowered), (b) that the crossing is not obstructed by a stationary or very slow-moving road vehicle, and (c) that the train can stop before reaching the crossing in the event of failure or obstruction. Automatic open crossings are cheaper to install than AHBs because the train driver does the monitoring of their operation locally, instead of remote operation (using expensive cable) by the signaller or other crossing operator. Also, in the case of AOCLs/AOCL-Bs, the road requirements are not so stringent as they are at AHB crossings. There are many level crossings on secondary lines, especially those operated on only two shifts, where an AHB crossing would have been too expensive, but where an economic case could be made for the installation of a locally monitored crossing.

There are restrictions on the provision of AOCL/AOCL-B crossings, depending upon the *traffic moment*, whereas the ABCL crossing has no such traffic restrictions; however, the ABCL crossing must satisfy some additional road conditions. Traffic moment denotes the combination of trains and road vehicles in any hour; for example, 15 road vehicles and two trains an hour would represent a traffic moment of 30.

The road traffic light signals (and the half barriers at ABCLs and AOCL-Bs) are operated automatically by the occupation of track circuits by approaching trains, supplemented by treadles at the strike-in point (owing to problems with the unreliability of track circuit operation by lightweight vehicles). A driver's crossing indicator facing the train driver is provided close to the crossing on each rail approach to the crossing. This displays a white flashing light when the road traffic light signals are operating correctly, and a flashing red light when the white light is not flashing.

The train driver is warned that the train is approaching a locally monitored crossing by a sign showing a black St George's cross on a white background (the advance warning board). The driver must then reduce speed (if necessary) so that the train will pass a special speed restriction board at the appropriate speed. On passing the special speed restriction board (with black numerals and a black St Andrew's cross on a white background), located at braking distance from the crossing, the driver must check that the crossing is clear and that the white light is flashing, then proceed to the crossing at the speed shown on the special speed restriction board, known as the *crossing speed*. The maximum crossing speed allowed is 56mph (90km/h).

If the white light adjacent to the crossing is not flashing, or if the crossing cannot be seen to be clear, or in other specified circumstances, the driver must stop short of the crossing and not proceed over it without ensuring that it is safe to do so. The horn must be sounded continuously until the front of the train is on the crossing. During darkness, however, a train must not pass over an AOCL crossing when the road traffic

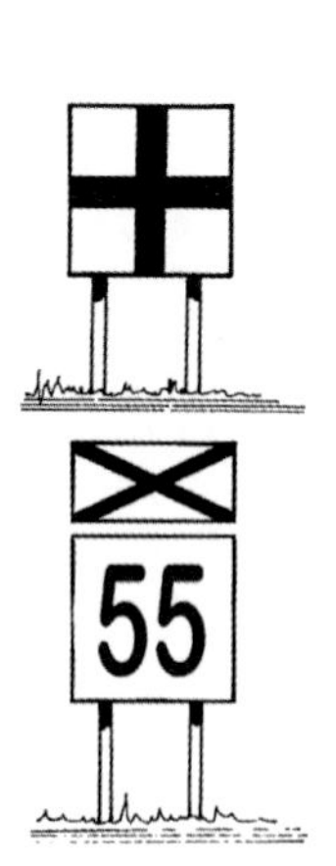

RIGHT Lineside signs warning the driver that the train is approaching an automatic locally monitored level crossing: the advance warning board (top) and the special speed restriction board.

ABOVE The driver's crossing indicator on the approach to Launton crossing. This normally displays a flashing red light but changes to a flashing white light when the road traffic light signals are flashing. Also to be seen is the small cabinet containing a plunger, which a train driver can use to operate the crossing manually if for some reason the train does not automatically initiate the crossing sequence. *Author*

signals have failed unless it is a passenger or empty coaching stock train with the lights on, or other safety arrangements have been made.

The operating cycle is as follows:

1. An amber light in each road traffic light signal shows for 3 seconds.
2. The twin red road traffic light signals start to flash alternately.
3. The train arrives at the crossing not less than 27 seconds after the amber lights first show.

The crossing speed is therefore determined by the braking distance available from the point at which the crossing comes into the driver's view, so that the train can stop safely before reaching the crossing if the driver sees that it is obstructed, or that the driver's crossing indicator has not changed from the flashing red light to the flashing white light. A sharply curved approach, where a crossing does not come into view until the train is fairly close to it, will therefore require a lower crossing speed than one that comes into clear view from a greater distance. The crossing speed board must not be more than 600 metres from the driver's crossing indicators at the crossing. In the case of AOCLs/AOCL-Bs, the crossing speed may be further reduced depending on the traffic moment.

Some speed restriction boards carry two figures. The bottom figure (the higher speed) applies to passenger trains, while the top figure (the lower speed) applies to all other trains.

Where an automatic open crossing is situated at or near the ends of station platforms, a special speed restriction board is not provided, but there is a 'STOP' board near the crossing. When the train is ready to restart, the driver presses a plunger that causes the road traffic signals to flash. The driver must check before starting and passing the 'STOP' board that the crossing is clear and that the white light is flashing, and must then sound the horn. At some places the flashing of the lights is started automatically, instead of manually by plunger.

As at automatic half barrier crossings, an audible warning for pedestrians is sounded at the crossing as a train approaches, and if the lights continue to flash after the train has passed over the crossing, the sound of the audible warning increases in frequency. There are no telephones at AOCLs/AOCL-Bs, but a plate gives the telephone number of a suitable railway office and also the name of the crossing.

Equipment is provided at some crossings to enable wrong-direction movements to be made in the normal way, similar to the arrangements at AHB-X crossings. These crossings are designated as ABCL-X and AOCL-X crossings.

CHAPTER 31

Other level crossings

Open crossings

Open level crossings are to be found on quiet single lines, where the traffic moment is not more than 30 in any hour. The crossings are non-automatic, there are no gates or barriers, and there are no flashing red road traffic light signals. Road signs require road users to give way to trains, and satisfactory visibility of approaching trains is necessary. Trains either approach the crossing at 15km/h (10mph), or stop at a 'Stop' board 25 metres from it. They must stop if the road users' view of approaching trains is inadequate (or vice versa). There are no telephones. There were 47 of these crossings on Network Rail in May 2016.

On the railway, an advance warning board is provided at braking distance to enable trains to reduce speed to 15km/h (10mph), or stop. The sign shows a black St George's cross on a white background. A speed restriction/whistle board is provided at a point from which the driver has a clear view of the crossing and from which the train can be stopped short of the crossing if necessary.

User-worked crossings

Almost all the level crossings considered in previous chapters have been on public roads, but the great majority of those that are dealt with in this chapter are private, and the public have no right to use them with a road vehicle,

BELOW A basic user-worked crossing with a public footpath crossing adjacent to it. The user-worked crossing has a telephone provided, for use when crossing with vehicles or animals, to confirm with the signaller that there is sufficient time to cross safely. *Author*

although there are public footpath or bridleway rights at some. Private crossings are of two types – *occupation crossings* and *accommodation crossings* – and in most cases consist of outward-opening farm-type gates on both sides of the railway, which normally bear a notice requiring the user to shut and fasten the gates after use, with a penalty for failure to do so. A very few user-worked crossings have barriers that are operated by a crossing user.

Occupation crossings are on private roads that existed before the railway was built. The road may have served only one farm, or it may have served several farms and/or cottages. When the railway was built, the tracks were laid across the private road, creating an occupation crossing. In addition to those who have a right to use the crossing by virtue of residence, others who have business there may also use the crossing, such as delivery workers and other tradespeople.

Accommodation crossings came about when the construction of a railway line divided a piece of land in single ownership into two pieces of land. In order to provide access from one part of the divided land to the other, accommodation bridges and level crossings had to be built, which frequently merely give access from a field on one side of the railway to another on the other side.

There are three levels of protection at user-worked crossings (figures are the number of each type on Network Rail in May 2016):

1. Crossings with no equipment (475)
2. Crossings equipped with a telephone (1,690)
3. Crossings equipped with *miniature stop lights* (97)

At crossings with no equipment, safety is reliant on the crossing user looking for approaching trains before making a decision whether or not to cross. Instructions as to how to use the crossing are provided at all user-worked crossings. Good viewing distances are essential, and to ensure safety the time taken for a train to arrive at the crossing from first being seen must be greater than the time taken to cross the railway. If a crossing user needs to take animals, or drive a long, low or slow-moving vehicle across the railway, the signaller must be contacted to get permission to cross. In the case of long, low or slow-moving vehicles, the signaller will provide signal protection before giving permission to the crossing user.

ABOVE The sign providing instructions on how to use a user-worked crossing provided with a telephone. The top sign applies to an adjacent public footpath crossing. *Author*

Where the *sighting distance* of trains from the crossing is inadequate, or herds of animals or heavy machinery are regularly taken over, a telephone to a signal box is provided so that the user can ask the signaller if the crossing may be used. On each occasion, the signaller must find out what is to be taken over the crossing, and the user must be informed if there is sufficient time for

ABOVE A typical public footpath crossing accessed through kissing gates on both sides of the railway. Others are protected by wicket gates or by stiles. *Author*

that movement to take place before the next train. If there is insufficient time, the signaller must tell the user to wait and telephone again. All calls that the signaller makes and receives are recorded.

User-worked crossings that have significant usage may be provided with miniature stop lights. These consist of small red and green lights, operated by approaching trains. The green light shows continuously until a train running at maximum line speed is about 40 seconds away, when it will be extinguished and the red light will show. If no light shows, the notice board warns the user to beware, or to telephone the signaller; a telephone may be provided if, for example, heavy farm plant or cattle are regularly taken over the crossing.

It should be noted that there are a few public level crossings that, for historical reasons, do not conform to the principles set out in Part 8.

Public footpath and bridleway crossings

In May 2016 there were 2,099 footpath and bridleway crossings on Network Rail. They are protected by stiles (footpath crossings only) or outward-opening wicket gates on each side of the railway. Crossing users have to exercise enough vigilance to cross safely, and sufficient warning time of approaching trains should be available to enable them to do so. 'Stop, look, listen' and 'Beware of Trains' signs are provided at each side.

Where there is insufficient sighting of approaching trains, 'whistle' boards may be provided not more than 400 metres (440 yards) from the crossing, or, where pedestrian usage is heavy, miniature stop lights may be provided. Telephones may be provided in the case of bridleway crossings.

Risk assessment

In recent years there has been a considerable focus on assessing the risk at level crossings, and a mathematical model known as the All Level Crossing Risk Model (ALCRM) has been developed to assist with this. This has enabled Network Rail to rank crossings according to their

ABOVE A user-worked crossing fitted with power-operated gate openers. *RAIB*

risk, so that efforts to reduce risk can be focused on those that justify it. An internet-based 'level crossing risk management toolkit' (www.lxrmtk.com) has been developed to provide risk assessors with a list of possible risk reduction measures depending on the specific circumstances at a crossing.

The safest crossing is a closed crossing and the railway industry has made, and continues to make, major efforts to close level crossings where it is possible to do so. This may require replacing the crossing with a bridge, at considerable trouble and expense.

New technology at level crossings

New technology is increasingly being applied to improve the safety of level crossings:

1. Light emitting diodes (LEDs) are now widely used for the road traffic light signals and miniature stop lights at level crossings. These are more conspicuous (and therefore more likely to be noticed) by crossing users.
2. Greater use of 'predictors' to ensure road users at automatic crossings have a constant warning time irrespective of the approach speed of a train. This should reduce the temptation that road users sometimes have to ignore the road traffic light signals.
3. An increase in the number of manually controlled barrier crossings with obstacle detection. These are likely to replace many automatic crossings.
4. Low-cost versions of miniature stop lights for user-worked crossings that can be overlaid on to the existing signalling system. These are likely to be provided at many crossings currently fitted with telephones to the signaller, and those with 'whistle' boards.
5. The fitment of power-operated gate openers at user-worked crossings to make it easier for users to operate the gates and to improve gate discipline.

PART 9

CHAPTER 32

Hot axle box and wheel impact load detectors

Hot axle box detectors

Hot axle box detectors are provided on main lines about every 32-40km (20-25 miles), especially where there are no lineside signal boxes, to check whether there are any overheated axle bearings in passing trains. If not detected, an overheated bearing could lead to a train's derailment or cause a fire. Signallers in lineside signal boxes are expected to look out for signs of hot axle boxes on passing trains, and have the trains stopped if necessary. Signallers can recognise a hot axle box in a number of ways – by the smell of overheated material, by the sight of smoke or flames, or by abnormal noises.

In the absence of a lineside signaller, hot axle boxes are detected by equipment located on the track. The *hot axle box detector* (HABD) scans the axle box passing over it for infrared radiation, which is emitted at normal and hot axle bearing temperatures. An alarm is sounded in the monitoring signal box if a hot axle bearing is detected.

If the alarm sounds in the signal box, the signaller will put the signals at danger to stop the train, and will also stop trains on adjoining lines until the train with the hot axle box has stopped and the driver has confirmed that no other lines are affected (by a derailed vehicle, for example). Immediately after placing the signals to danger, the signaller must contact operations control to see whether the vehicle concerned is conveying dangerous goods.

When the driver reports to the signaller (normally by telephone), the signaller must tell the driver the axle number, counting from the front of the train (including the locomotive) and whether left-hand or right-hand side (the signal box equipment displays these details). The driver must then examine the axle box concerned for evidence of overheating, if necessary by feeling it or using a device known as a Tempilstik, and report what is found to the signaller.

If the axle box is obviously hot, but the vehicle concerned is safe to be moved, it must be detached in a nominated siding, to which the train must travel at a speed not exceeding 15km/h (10mph) on plain line and 10km/h (5mph) over points and crossings. If it is a passenger coach, the passengers should be moved out of the vehicle before detaching takes place. The signaller must stop trains on adjoining lines before authorising the driver to make the movement.

If no defect can be found, the train may proceed normally, but a further examination must be carried out within 80km (50 miles) by either a rolling stock technician or the driver, unless the train passes over a hot axle box detector in working order without activating the alarm. If further examination reveals that there is nothing wrong, the train may resume its normal journey. If, however, the second detector sounds an alarm and the train has to be moved, its speed must not exceed 30km/h (20mph).

These instructions do not apply to steam locomotives in steam, which, by their very nature, are liable to cause false alarms.

Wheel impact load detectors

Wheel impact load detectors, known by the brand names 'WheelChex' and 'Gotcha' (the latter system is replacing WheelChex), are installed on the network to measure the impact loads of each wheel of a train and to measure whether these loads are outside acceptable limits, for example because of damage such as wheel flats or an out-of-round wheel. These conditions, if not detected, could cause damage to the track or increase the risk of derailment. The system also provides data on overloaded vehicles, or vehicles with offset loads.

If an unacceptable wheel load is measured by the system, an alarm sounds in the local operations control and a controller will then contact the appropriate signaller so that the train can be stopped for examination by the driver. Depending on the outcome, the train may be terminated or allowed to proceed forward at reduced speed.

CHAPTER 33

Permanent speed restrictions

All Network Rail's running lines are engineered and maintained for trains to run at specific speeds, and these are the maximum permissible speeds for the route concerned. They are published in a document known as the *Sectional Appendix*. These speeds, known as *permissible speeds*, are not constant throughout the route, but vary over different sections. The maximum permissible speed is indicated at the lineside by retroreflective circular signs with black numerals and a red border (the older version of the sign, consisting of yellow cut-out numerals, can also still be seen).

At certain places on the route, speed has to be reduced below the normal line speed owing, for example, to sharp curvature or the complexity of the track layout. These reductions of speed are known as permanent speed restrictions (PSR).

To assist the driver when approaching the location of a permissible speed reduction at 60mph (97km/h) or more, where the train's speed must be reduced by a third or more, an advance warning sign, known as a warning indicator, must normally be provided, sufficiently far back to allow the driver time to reduce speed to the required level. The warning indicator takes the form of a reflectorised triangular sign with black numerals and a yellow border. In addition, an AWS permanent magnet is normally provided 180 metres (200 yards) on the approach side of the sign, so that an audible warning is given in the driving cab to alert the driver to the restriction ahead. The brakes are applied automatically if the driver does not acknowledge the warning.

Since the introduction of TPWS fitted to signals, that system has also been provided at many of those PSRs meeting the criteria in the above paragraph. A TPWS overspeed sensor is fitted 400-600 metres (440-660 yards) before the commencement of the speed restriction and the brakes are applied automatically if the driver has

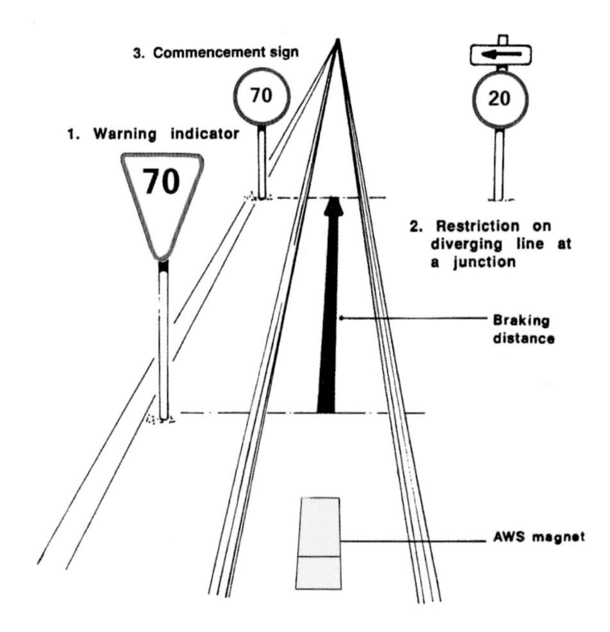

RIGHT Permanent speed restriction signs

not reduced the train's speed to less than the speed setting of the TPWS.

The approach speed is considered to be the maximum permissible speed on the immediate approach to the restriction, but a lower speed may be assumed in certain circumstances.

Where there is a 'cascade' of speed restrictions (two or more within 3.2km/2 miles), none of which may individually justify a warning indicator, but where there is a total speed reduction of more than a third between the approach speed to the first restriction and the last in the cascade, a warning indicator is provided for the PSR, which takes the total reduction in speed to more than a third.

Where the warning indicator and/or permissible *speed indicator* applies to a diverging line, it will carry an arrow, pointing left or right as appropriate. Where differential speeds apply, the warning indicator and the permissible speed indicator will show two speeds, one above the other. The bottom figure, showing the higher speed, applies only to passenger (loaded or empty), postal and parcels trains, and to light locomotives. The top figure (the lower speed) applies to all other trains.

Where the indicators show letters above the numerals, the meaning is as follows:

HST New-generation diesel multiple units (except Class 185), Class 220, 221 and 222 trains, Class 91 locomotives with Mark 4 coaches and Driving Van Trailer, Class 253 and 254 High Speed Trains, Class 373 Eurostar trains, and Class 390 'Pendolino' trains
MU Multiple unit trains (except Class 185)
DMU Diesel multiple unit trains (except Class 185)
EMU Electric multiple unit trains
SP Class 150-159 ('Sprinter'-type) trains, Class 165 and 166, Class 168, 170 and 171 ('Turbostars')
CS Class 67 locomotives

Where both HST and SP speeds apply at a location, trains of Classes 168, 170 and 171 are permitted to run at the higher of the two speeds.

As described in Chapter 25, enhanced permissible speed (EPS) signs show the permissible speeds for tilting trains (Class 221, in tilting mode, and 390). The figure on the sign denotes the maximum EPS for the section of line ahead, and above the figure are the letters 'EPS'. In some cases a differential enhanced permissible speed applies where the bottom (higher) speed applies to Class 390 trains and the top (lower) speed applies to Class 221 trains in tilting mode. Warning indicators replicate the information provided on the EPS signs.

Complications may arise where reductions of speed are necessary for two or more separate but adjoining permanent speed restrictions, where the warning board for the second restriction would otherwise precede the commencement sign for the first one. In such cases special arrangements may apply.

The location of the warning indicator is based on the distance needed to reduce speed to the required level from the maximum permitted approach speed, based on braking curves. The distance may be extended to ensure that the associated AWS magnet is at least 4 seconds from any other magnet.

CHAPTER 34

Temporary speed restrictions

Temporary speed restrictions (TSRs) are imposed as follows:

1. Where the track is not in a fit condition for trains to run on at the normal permissible speed, usually pending or following maintenance or renewals
2. To enhance the safety of staff working on an adjacent line(s).

The driver is informed of such restrictions by:

1. An entry in the *Weekly Operating Notice*, issued to all drivers, which contains a section listing all TSRs, route by route, for the area concerned
2. A notice in a special *late notice case* at the depot where the driver signs on duty. Drivers are required to read such notices every time they sign on duty.
3. Signs erected at the lineside, supplemented by an AWS permanent magnet

The lineside signs are as follows:

1. A warning board, positioned on the left-hand side of the line at braking distance from the start of the TSR, and denoting the speed limit of the TSR. If it is a TSR beyond a diverging junction, the warning board will carry a directional arrow, called a *directional indicator*. Differential speed restrictions may apply, in which case the bottom figure showing the higher speed applies only to passenger trains (loaded or empty), postal and parcels trains, and to light locomotives, while the top figure

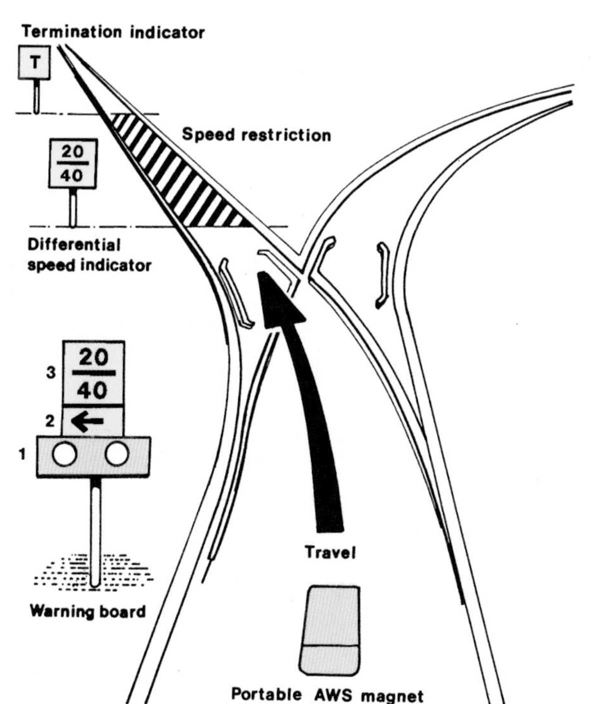

LEFT Temporary speed restriction signs: (1)warning board, (2) applicable to the diverging route, and (3) differential speed indicator

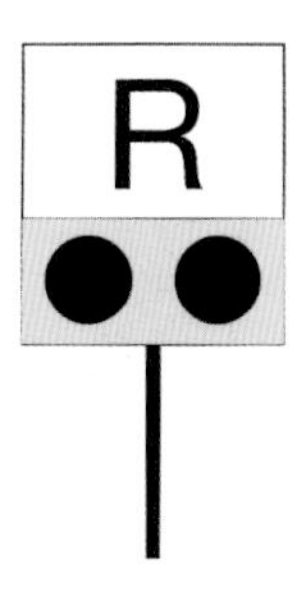

ABOVE Reflectorised repeating warning board at platform departure end

(the lower speed) applies to all other trains.
2. A speed indicator at the start of the restriction, showing the permitted speed
3. A termination indicator at the end of the restriction

Where the normal position of a warning board falls on the approach side of a passenger station, a siding connection or a dead-end platform line, and the speed indicator is more than 300 metres (about 330 yards) ahead of that location, a *repeating warning board* is provided at the far end of the platform (or other appropriate location) as a reminder to the driver. The repeating warning board is a retroreflective sign with a horizontal yellow bar including two white discs, and with the letter 'R' above the bar.

The warning board, speed indicator and termination indicator are also retroreflective. The warning board consists of a horizontal yellow bar containing two discs with the TSR value on a sign above the horizontal bar.

A portable AWS permanent magnet is placed in the 'four-foot' 180 metres (200 yards) on the approach side of the warning board, but where the appropriate location for the magnet falls near to a signal or its AWS magnets, it may be more convenient for the warning board to be placed at the signal, and for the signal magnet to be adjusted so that only a warning indication can be given, irrespective of the aspect being shown by the signal.

Special arrangements for the location of warning boards, etc, apply where there are two adjacent TSRs.

A TSR may be withdrawn or eased earlier than shown in the Weekly Operating Notice, in which case the warning board and speed indicator will be altered to show the higher speed. If a TSR shown in the Weekly Operating Notice is not imposed, the warning board, etc, must be erected unless a special notice cancelling the TSR has been issued at least 24 hours before the time it was due to start. The warning board and speed indicator must be altered to show a 'SPATE' ('speed previously advised terminated early') indication (see the accompanying drawing).

If a TSR is withdrawn earlier than shown, or is not imposed, the speed indication in both the warning board and the speed indicator may be replaced by a *SPATE Indicator*. Where there are TSRs on both routes at a diverging junction and the correct positions of both warning boards fall on the approach side of the junction, the second warning board must be positioned at least 45 metres (50 yards) beyond the first. The second warning board will have an AWS magnet.

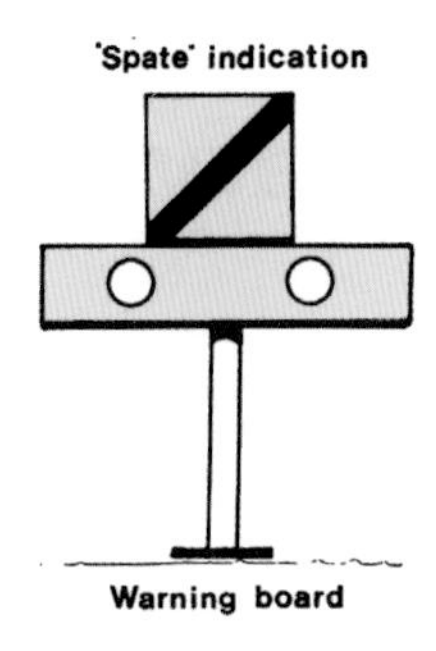

ABOVE A 'SPATE' indicator denotes that a restriction has been withdrawn or has not been imposed.

The driver must not resume normal speed until the whole of the train has passed clear of the TSR.

A missing warning board, etc, must be dealt with as follows:

1. Warning board or speed indicator missing, in the wrong place or more restrictive than previously published in the Weekly Operating Notice: the driver must tell the signaller at once, stopping the train specially if necessary. The signaller must warn all other drivers about it and tell operations control.
2. Warning board, a speed or termination indicator that is becoming difficult to see: the driver must tell the signaller at the first convenient opportunity, and the signaller must tell operations control.

If a TSR does not finish on time, it must be dealt with as an emergency speed restriction.

Emergency Temporary Speed Restrictions (ESRs)

When it is necessary to impose an ESR without notice to drivers, special steps must be taken to ensure that drivers are aware of it and do not take their trains over the ESR at more than the appropriate speed. The signaller must be told at once, and equipment must be provided without delay, and a *special notice* issued, if the restriction is to continue for more than a short time.

The sequence of events after the need to impose an ESR has come to light is as follows:

1. If possible, trains should be diverted to another line or route until the equipment has been provided.
2. If it is necessary for trains to pass over the ESR before equipment is in position, the signaller must stop all trains on the line affected and explain the situation to the driver, ensuring that the driver correctly understands exactly where the ESR is, and the speed limit over it. The train may then be allowed to proceed.
3. A warning board, portable AWS magnet, speed indicator and termination indicator must be erected under the same arrangements as for a TSR.
4. An *emergency indicator*, consisting of a board with black and yellow chevrons and two brilliant white flashing lights mounted vertically, must be erected not more than 400 metres (440 yards) and not less than 180 metres (200 yards) on the approach side of the warning board, together with a portable AWS magnet 180 metres (200 yards) before the emergency indicator. If the warning board is located less than 400 metres (440 yards) beyond a *fixed signal* equipped with AWS, the emergency indicator must be erected at the signal, and the AWS electromagnet must be disconnected so that a driver will receive a warning irrespective of the aspect being displayed at the signal. In such circumstances, an additional portable magnet is not required.

The emergency indicator must remain in position until details of the ESR are shown in the Weekly Operating Notice or the restriction is withdrawn. The emergency indicator lights must be lit at all times. If the indicator fails, the driver must tell the signaller at once, stopping specially if necessary. The signaller must inform all drivers affected and arrange for the emergency indicator to be repaired or replaced.

If a blanket emergency speed restriction has to be applied – for example, because of adverse weather affecting the infrastructure – this will be done by operations control, which will advise signallers and train operating companies; emergency indicators and other associated track equipment will not be provided.

A TSR that has a lower speed than that shown in the Weekly Notice, or applies at a different time, must be treated as an ESR

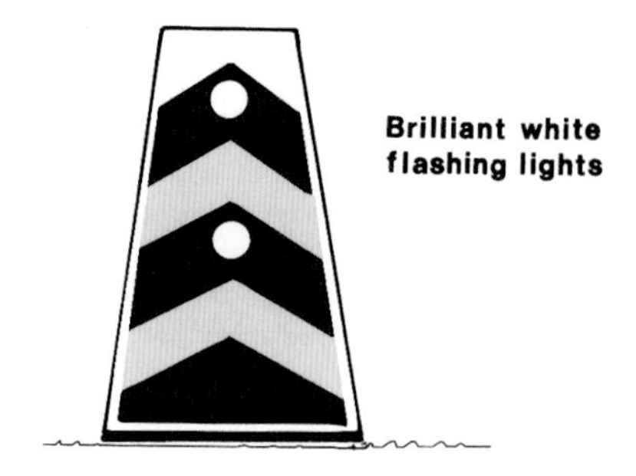

ABOVE Emergency indicator for an emergency speed restriction ahead

PART 10

CHAPTER 35

Train radio systems

The standard radio system fitted to all driving cabs of trains running on Network Rail is the Global System for Mobile Communications – Railways (GSM-R). This provides track-to-train communications and is also a constituent part of ERTMS, providing the transmission link between the control centre and trains. At the time of writing, GSM-R has just replaced the legacy radio systems, which had been in use for many years: *Cab Secure Radio* (CSR) and the *National Radio Network* (NRN).

NRN was first installed in about 1980 to provide radio communication between the operations control office and personnel out on the line, and allowed the more efficient management of engineer's possessions of the line. The system took a long time to reach its full potential due to the unreliability of the software and inadequate radio coverage, but additional base stations were provided to give almost complete coverage of the railway system.

NRN was not classed as a secure radio system, since there was no correlation between the train's radio call number and the train description number. The signaller was not normally aware of the radio call number of a particular train, and drivers usually initiated the radio traffic.

CSR was designed in the late 1970s to be installed in those trains that were to be operated without guards, now known as driver-only-operation (DOO), because the provision of this type of secure radio system was one of the safety requirements agreed between the British Railways Board and the Railway Inspectorate for the operation of suburban passenger trains without guards. It subsequently came to be used more generally, forming the normal method of communication between driver and signaller in suburban areas.

The signaller could initiate a call to a driver at any time and could ascertain at once from the signalling control panel where the train was, by looking for the train description number. Strict radio procedures were followed, although the system was designed to ensure that the signaller knew which driver was being spoken to. Radio messages between a signaller and a driver could not be overheard by other drivers, but the signaller could, if necessary, broadcast a general message to all drivers in a particular area.

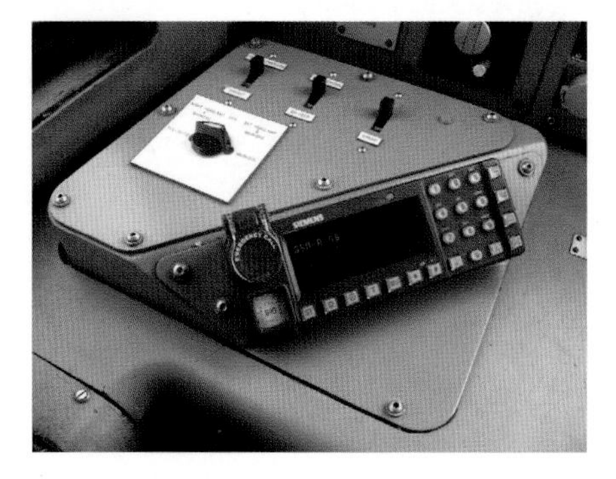

ABOVE The GSM-R console in an HST driving cab. *Peter van der Mark*

Global System for Mobile Communications – Railways (GSM-R)

By the early 1990s it had become clear that NRN and CSR were technically obsolescent. Other comparable systems elsewhere in Europe were also in need of replacement, so the opportunity was taken to develop a new specification that would be mandatory throughout the European Union. This led to a decision to adopt the GSM system, which would not only be a replacement for both NRN and CSR but also act as the bearer for the new European Train Control System (ETCS).

One of the main constituents of the GSM-R system is the *base transmitting station* (BTS). These stations are spaced around 8 to 20km apart and provide the transmitter/receiver points at the lineside. The BTS consists of a radio station, power supply and a tower or mast and the aerials. Around 3,000 BTSs are required alongside the railway network.

The term 'mobile' in GSM-R refers to the equipment fitted to all driving cabs, and to portable handsets that can be used by railway staff. Once the infrastructure for GSM-R has been

ABOVE A GSM-R base transmission station. This example is by the lineside at Wrawby Junction, Barnetby. *Author*

fitted to the whole network and all driving cabs have been equipped, NRN and CSR will no longer be used and the equipment will be removed.

Before a train leaves its starting point, GSM-R must be registered to the network, after which it is live. It provides direct communication between driver and signaller and vice versa. Besides routine communications, GSM-R can also be used when an emergency arises:

1. To make an urgent call to a signaller when there is no need to stop other trains, but where the safety of the line on which the train concerned is travelling may be affected, for example where the driver has seen and/or felt a track defect. To initiate this type of call, the driver simply presses a yellow button on the radio console.
2. To make an emergency group call to stop all trains in the area when the safety of the line is affected. The driver presses a red button on the radio console to initiate this type of call.
3. When the Train Signalling Regulations require the signaller to stop a train in an emergency, the signaller must use radio if this might enable the train to be stopped more quickly. Signallers can use GSM-R to send emergency broadcast calls to one train or to all drivers in an area, for example to instruct the drivers to stop their trains.

Drivers and signallers can also exchange text messages using GSM-R, and there is the facility for drivers to send a 'stood at (red) signal' text message, obviating the need for the driver to climb down from the driving cab to use the signal post telephone. A signaller may also send a text message asking a driver to make contact. All signal box telephone numbers are contained in the radio system's memory.

CHAPTER 36

Engineering operations on the line

Introduction

If the line becomes unsafe for various reasons, such as landslip, flooding or washout, or when it requires repair or renewal, it is necessary to ensure that no train can enter the section of line affected. The arrangements for ensuring the safety of trains are of three kinds:

1. Protection when the line is unsafe
2. Protection of engineering work being carried out under a line blockage
3. Protection of engineering work being carried out under a possession

Protection when the line is unsafe

When the line is unsafe for trains to run on it, the following actions must be carried out:

1. The signaller must be advised so that signal protection can be provided as soon as possible.
2. A track circuit operating clip must be placed on the line affected to place signals to danger (note that this will only work if the line is track-circuited).
3. If the signaller cannot be contacted to provide signal protection, *detonator protection* must be provided.

Detonator protection consists of placing three detonators on the line, 20 metres (22 yards) apart, 2km (1¼ miles) away. However, in the following circumstances the three detonators must be placed on the line immediately, before reaching that distance:

1. If a train is approaching
2. If the person carrying out the duty reaches a signal box or telephone communicating with a signal box before that distance, in which case the detonators need not be placed at the full distance if the signaller advises that protection is being given by signals.
3. After switching a signal to danger by means of a *signal post replacement switch*
4. Before entering a tunnel. If the 2km (1¼-mile) point falls within the tunnel, the detonators must be placed at the far end of it.
5. Just before a trailing junction. Both legs of the junction must be protected, and it is a question of judgement as to which is done first.

The person concerned must remain at the detonators showing a red flag or lamp until the line is again safe for trains to pass.

Protection of engineering work being carried out under a line blockage

This method of protection is for work that can be carried out without disruption to the normal running of trains. The work is protected by maintaining at danger any signal(s) in the direction that trains may approach the site of work.

The work should be planned in advance wherever possible to minimise interference with the running of trains. The persons responsible for arranging protection must be qualified to do so, and are known as either the *safe work leader* (SWL) or the *controller of site safety* (COSS). The SWL or COSS must make appropriate arrangements with the signaller, such as the lines to be blocked, the location of the work and the time needed to do it, and the signal(s) that need to be maintained at danger to protect the work being undertaken.

Before the signaller will issue an *authority number* to authorise the work to take place, one or more of the following additional protection measures must be carried out:

1. The disconnection of signalling equipment by a signal technician to ensure that the protecting signal(s) cannot be changed from a stop aspect
2. The placing of one or more track circuit operating devices (T-COD) on the track. The signaller must check that each track circuit concerned is initially clear but shows occupied when the T-COD is applied.
3. The placing of detonator protection at the protecting signal(s)

4. The possession by the SWL/COSS of the single-line token for the line
5. The signaller applying reminder devices in the signal box

When the SWL/COSS has been issued with an authority number, a red flag (or red light) must be put in place that is clearly visible to the driver of any train approaching the work area.

These arrangements may also be used to safeguard anyone working on or near the line who may be endangered by passing trains, or when cranes or other mechanical equipment that may foul the line are being used.

Protection of engineering work being carried out under a possession

These arrangements are put in place for more major work in which one or more of the running lines is blocked to the normal running of trains. Possessions are normally used whenever engineering operations are to be carried out using engineer's trains or on-track machines or plant. Within the length of the possession, there may be several worksites where the actual work takes place, and the possession may extend for many miles, although its length should be kept to a minimum as the normal signalling arrangements are suspended. No train other than an engineer's train may pass through a possession.

Unless the circumstances are urgent, the possession of a running line must be planned in advance and published in the railway's operating notices.

The arrangements for ensuring safety are detailed and lengthy, and fall under the following headings:

1. Appointment of specific people with special responsibilities
2. Protection of the possession
3. Control of the movement of trains from the 'live' railway into the area of the possession
4. Protection of individual worksites
5. Control of the movement of trains within the possession
6. Control of the movement of trains from the possession into the 'live' railway
7. Giving up the possession

The word 'train' includes engineer's on-track machines such as tamping machines, ballast regulators, etc, whereas other plant such as road-rail vehicles and rail-mounted maintenance machines are known as *possession only rail vehicles* and not permitted to work or run outside possessions.

Appointment of specific people

The key roles are as follows:

1. The *person in charge of the possession (PICOP)*, who must be certified as competent and familiar with the line and the arrangements, and must normally have no other responsibilities
2. The safe work leader or engineering supervisor in charge of each worksite
3. The safe work leader or controller of site safety in charge of each work group, or several groups, within a worksite

Each of these wears an appropriately worded armband to indicate to others who they are.

Protection of the possession

Protection is given by fixed signals and by detonators, three of which are positioned 20 metres (22 yards) apart at both ends of the possession. The first set of detonators is generally placed 400 metres (¼ mile) beyond the protecting signal; those at the other end of the possession are generally placed 400 metres (¼ mile) before a stop signal. A *possession limit board* consisting of a stop sign and flashing red light is placed next to the centre detonator. The protection is intended not only to prevent a train from straying wrongly into the possession, but also to prevent a train from straying from inside the possession on to the 'live' railway.

Trains entering the possession

The signaller must not allow a train to proceed towards the protecting detonators from either end without the PICOP's permission. Having obtained this permission, the signaller must tell the driver what is happening and that the train may pass the protecting signal at danger and proceed cautiously to the protecting detonators, from which point the PICOP will authorise the next movement.

75
MU
90

20

TOP LEFT Minor engineering work is taking place under a possession of both lines at Craven Arms on the North and West route. A tamping machine is standing outside the signal box among the BR Western Region-pattern lower-quadrant semaphore signals. *Author*

BOTTOM LEFT Seen from Craven Arms station footbridge, the marker boards denoting the limits of the worksite can be seen together with the possession limit board on the line that trails in from Knighton (the Central Wales Line). *Author*

Protection of individual worksites

Worksites within a possession must normally be indicated by marker boards. The exceptions are where there are no engineer's trains or on-track machines within the possession, or there is only one worksite, and the only movements are on-track machines. The marker boards are double-sided and have two flashing lights, arranged vertically. Red lights indicate the entrance to the worksite; the board is not to be passed unless the safe work leader/engineering supervisor authorises it. Yellow lights indicate the exit from the worksite, and the board is not to be passed without the PICOP's authority. The boards must be positioned at least 100 metres (100 yards) from the end of the worksite.

Control of the movement of trains within the possession

Since the normal signalling arrangements are suspended during a possession, all movements must be authorised verbally. The only people authorised to do so are the PICOP and, within a given worksite, the safe work leader/engineering supervisor. All other movements are authorised by the PICOP. Propelling movements are allowed under special conditions. These aspects of the possession arrangements need very careful handling, in view of the variety of movements and hazards that can occur, especially as engineering work is often carried out at night. Trains may move in either direction, they may be split into one or more sections, they may be propelled, they may be stationary, there may be noisy machinery, and there are likely to be a large number of workers both on the trains and on the track.

Trains leaving the possession

The PICOP must tell the signaller when any movement is ready to leave the possession. The signaller then gives authority for such a movement.

Giving up the possession

Giving up the possession is one of the most critical activities, since it is essential to ensure that all trains, machines and equipment have been removed from the possession, that all workers on site are aware that the possession is being given up, and that the line is safe for trains to run on. This is the PICOP's responsibility, who will receive a written certificate from each safe work leader/engineering supervisor to that effect. The PICOP can then tell the signaller that it is now possible to give up the possession and remove the protection.

Note: The contents of this chapter are only intended to be a brief summary of the arrangements and do not apply to High Speed 1 from St Pancras International through the Channel Tunnel, or to the ERTMS-fitted lines in mid-Wales, where different arrangements apply.

PART 12

CHAPTER 37

Future developments

The development of signalling technology, both by the railway undertakings themselves and by the national and international signalling contractors, has been a continuous process, although its application to Britain's railways has been marked by a series of major advances:

1. The invention of the track circuit
2. The application of electric power to the operation of points
3. The introduction of the electrically lit colour light signal
4. The replacement of mechanical interlocking by electrical relay interlocking
5. The one-control switch (OCS) system of setting a route and clearing signals, allowing one signal box to control a large area
6. The refinement of the OCS system into the entrance/exit (NX) system, which became the British Railways standard in the 1960s
7. The application of solid-state computer technology to signalling interlocking, replacing relays
8. The adoption of visual display units in signalling centre operating rooms, replacing the large indication panels
9. The use of trackerballs and keyboards, instead of push-buttons on large control panels, for use by the signaller in controlling points and signals
10. The use of radio for vital signalling messages, as in the Radio Electronic Token Block system
11. The application of computers to the automation of route-setting
12. The implementation of train protection systems ranging from AWS to TPWS and ATP
13. The use of cab signalling, now implemented for trains on High Speed 1, which will be an inherent feature of the European Train Control System eventually to be installed throughout the network

The speed at which modern signalling developments are adopted depends on a number of factors, such as the availability of finance, the capital cost of new equipment, the benefits it might provide in greater reliability and reduced maintenance and operating costs, and the need for improved safety levels.

The factors that lead to existing signalling being replaced in more modern form are:

1. Existing equipment becoming life-expired
2. Electrification schemes, which normally entail major resignalling, both for technical reasons and to cater for higher speeds and altered track layouts
3. Changes in traffic patterns and levels, leading to the need either to reduce signalling costs or to cater for increased traffic levels
4. Conurbation area schemes for improved passenger train services, frequently promoted by local authorities and passenger transport executives
5. The desire of train operators for higher speeds

Future developments over the next few years were fully described in Chapter 3, but can be summarised as:

1. The concentration of signalling control in Rail Operating Centres (ROCs) to eventually cover the entire railway network
2. The implementation of traffic management, integrating signalling control with traffic control, with new tools to optimise decision-making during perturbed operation
3. Further fitments of modular signalling on the less busy routes as a lower-cost alternative to standard resignalling
4. Further installations of manually controlled barrier crossings with obstacle detection and lower-cost warning systems at user-worked crossings
5. The introduction of ERTMS/ETCS to main-line operation

Network Rail has decided on a policy of concentrating signal operation in ROCs to cover the entire network, allowing the closure of the existing signalling control centres and other signal boxes.

On much of the network, the ROCs may simply recontrol the existing signalling equipment where this is not life-expired. This may either be remotely through the existing interlockings, still in situ at control centres that have otherwise been closed, or through new interlockings. The implementation of this policy is likely to take many years.

Traditional traffic control offices are also being located in the ROCs, together with the control of electrification equipment. The integration of traffic control with signalling control gives rise to the need for tools that will aid and optimise decision-making in the regulation of trains, particularly during periods of perturbed operation. This is the purpose of a Traffic Management System, which is likely to be implemented widely over the coming years.

Modular signalling has been developed as a lower-cost means of resignalling less busy secondary and rural routes, enabling the closure of small signal boxes controlling mechanical signalling equipment. Each item of equipment is deemed to be a standardised module in which much of the testing can be carried out off-site. These are then put together on site as required to create the resignalled route.

In the area of level crossings, the manually controlled barrier crossing with obstacle detection has been developed. As well as removing the human element from the operation of crossings, they relieve signaller workload, necessary to enable ROCs to cover large areas of the network, which may contain many level crossings. Also necessary are new forms of protection at the many user-worked level crossings to reduce the number of calls that signallers have to deal with from users and to improve their safety more generally. Low-cost warning systems have been developed and are likely to see widespread fitment.

Overlying all these developments is the more widespread fitment of ERTMS/ETCS; not only is this necessary on account of EU requirements relating to the Trans-European network, but also to obtain the capacity benefits necessary to accommodate a growing railway and to achieve greater efficiency of operation and cost. In time, this is likely to lead to the disappearance of lineside signals, except in more complex areas where limited installations are still likely to be needed. In the central area of the Thameslink system, *automatic train operation* in combination with ETCS is planned. This is necessary in order that the required number of trains per hour can be delivered. There will still be a driver on board.

Automatic control of the driving of trains is already in operation on certain Metro lines in Britain and abroad, but whether such a system would ever be applied to the driving of main-line trains is questionable. A driver is required for other purposes besides the normal driving of the train, such as:

1. Keeping a lookout for workers on the track, and sounding the horn to warn them of the train's approach
2. Keeping a lookout and sounding the horn when approaching level crossings
3. Keeping a lookout for anything that might be a hazard to trains (the driver's own or others), such as flood damage, bridge damage caused by road vehicles, obstructions on the line, (either accidental or deliberate), defective track, and animals on the line
4. Being on hand to deal with traction failures
5. Working through a section under caution for a whole variety of reasons, e.g. signalling and track circuit failures, defective track, vandalism, obstructions, animals on the line, examination of the line

There is little point in automating the driving of trains unless the cost of the driver can be avoided, so since it seems likely, for the reasons given above, that drivers will continue to be required for purposes other than normal driving, there is little likelihood of any train operator incurring heavy expenditure in automating the driving of trains, except perhaps in special situations.

Now that collisions and derailments caused by SPADs and overspeeding have been considerably reduced by the installation of TPWS, and will be reduced still further with the installation of ERTMS/ETCS, the outstanding safety issue is becoming the interaction of trains and road vehicles, not merely at level crossings but also at bridges both under and over the railway. It is not possible to eliminate collisions between road vehicles and trains, but improved front-end protection of trains, incorporating obstruction deflectors, can avoid them becoming derailed after a collision with a road vehicle. Highway authorities must also be proactive in managing the risk of road vehicles escaping from the road on to the railway.

Appendix

Regulatory authorities and their function

The Office of Rail and Road (ORR) is both the economic and the safety regulator of the main-line railway network. It incorporated the former safety regulator, HM Railway Inspectorate (HMRI), into its structure following HMRI's transfer to the ORR from the Health & Safety Executive in 2006.

The safety regulator has a number of functions, which include investigating accidents and incidents to see whether and to what extent health and safety law has been breached; issuing certificates to railway operators when it has agreed a statement of their safety management arrangements; carrying out inspections and audits of selected railway activities; issuing guidance on how to comply with the law; and taking formal enforcement action. The safety regulator has the power to issue enforcement notices and to carry out the prosecution of offenders. Enforcement notices can either require improvements to be carried out to an agreed timescale or, where a serious risk of personal injury is found to exist, an inspector can issue a notice prohibiting the activity.

The role that HMRI used to have in investigating railway accidents to find out the cause and make recommendations has been transferred to the Rail Accident Investigation Branch (RAIB). The RAIB became operational in October 2005 and was formed as the result of a recommendation arising from the inquiry into the serious train accident at Ladbroke Grove on 5 October 1999. It was also a requirement of a European Directive that the two functions of safety regulation and accident investigation should be dealt with by separate organisations. The RAIB's purpose is to improve the safety of the railways in the UK by investigating railway accidents and incidents and making recommendations to avoid a recurrence. The RAIB investigates only accidents involving moving trains, or matters arising from the operation of trains – not, for example, slips, trips and falls at stations, which remain with the safety regulator. All of the RAIB's investigation reports and current investigations are included on its website.

The RAIB has no powers to require its recommendations to be implemented. However, the ORR must monitor their implementation and report progress back to the RAIB at regular intervals. If necessary, the ORR has the powers described above to require recommendations to be implemented. The ORR will also consider and may agree any representations from a railway undertaking that believes a recommendation issued to it is unreasonable.

The Rail Safety and Standards Board (trading as RSSB) was established in April 2003, taking over the functions of the former Railway Safety organisation and before that the Safety and Standards Directorate of Railtrack. RSSB is a not-for-profit company that is owned by the industry itself and exists to further the improvement of safety on Britain's railways. It manages the Railway Group Standards (such as the Rule Book), publishes an annual safety plan, sponsors research and development work, monitors safety performance, supports cross-industry groups dealing with particular safety issues, and represents the UK railway industry on European matters.

Glossary

Technical terms and abbreviations

Absolute block – a signalling system that allows only one train to be between two signal boxes on the same line at the same time

Acceptance – a term used in absolute block signalling when a signaller allows a train to proceed from the adjacent signal box

Accommodation crossing – a private crossing connecting land that was separated when the railway was constructed

Annunciator – an audible alert that sounds in a signal box/control centre

Approach control – the clearing of a colour light signal when the approaching train has been proved to have reduced speed sufficiently to observe the correct speed over a junction/route

Approach locking – a system of locking facing points so that they cannot be moved across in front of an approaching train

Approach release – the point at which an approach-controlled signal is released to show a proceed or less restrictive aspect

Aspect – the coloured light or lights displayed by a colour light signal

Automatic barrier crossing, locally monitored (ABCL) – a level crossing with half barriers, the operation of which is initiated by an approaching train and whose operation is monitored by the train driver

Automatic half barrier crossing (AHB) – a level crossing with half barriers, the operation of which is initiated automatically by an approaching train

Automatic open crossing, locally monitored (AOCL) – a level crossing the operation of which is initiated by an approaching train and whose operation is monitored by the train driver. Many have been subsequently fitted with half barriers (AOCL-B).

Automatic route setting (ARS) – a computerised system for setting routes according to a pre-programmed formula

Automatic section – an automatically signalled section on an absolute block line

Automatic signal – a signal that is operated by the passage of trains

Automatic train control (ATC) – a former safety device for warning a driver of the need to slow down or stop

Automatic train operation (ATO) – a computer-based system that relieves the driver of the task of driving the train between stations. It is a non-safety system and must be combined with an Automatic Train Protection system. Generally found in Metro-type railways.

Automatic train protection (ATP) – a safety system for ensuring that the driver slows down or stops when necessary

Automatic warning system (AWS) – a track inductor-based system linked to the aspects of fixed lineside signals that provides audible and visual warnings to the driver on the approach to signals, certain level crossings and emergency, temporary and certain permanent speed restrictions

Axle counter – track-mounted equipment that counts the number of axles on a train as it passes

Back drive – a second drive (sometimes called a supplementary drive) that assists with the moving of the switch blades from one position to another and to maintain the flangeway clearance between the open switch rail and the stock rail

Banner repeating signal – a signal that gives a driver advance information about a signal that has limited sighting distance

Berth track circuit – the track circuit immediately before and up to a home signal

Block indicator – an instrument that indicates the state of the line between adjacent manual signal boxes

Blocking back – a term used in absolute block when a train or shunting movement is to be allowed to stand within the clearing point or outside the home signal

Block section – in absolute block, the section of line between the section signal of one signal box and the home signal of the next signal box ahead

Block signalling – a system of signalling based on block sections

Block switch – a switch enabling a signal box to be closed by putting the signal boxes on each side into through communication with each other

Block telephone – a telephone link between two adjacent signal boxes, using the block telegraph wires

Braking distance – the distance a train requires in which to stop from a given speed

Bridge bashing – overheight road vehicles colliding with railway bridges over the road

Cab secure radio (CSR) – a legacy radio system that provided a secure form of communication between driver and signaller

Cab signalling – a signalling system where train speed and braking are supervised by the system on the basis of movement authorities issued to a defined point ahead, indicated by a block marker sign at the lineside. Fitted to trains on High Speed 1 and lines signalled by the European Train Control System (ETCS)

Calling-on signal – a signal that, when cleared, allows a train into an already occupied section

Clear signal – a colour light signal displaying a green aspect, or a semaphore stop signal in the 'off' position

Clearing point – the point to which the line must be clear before a train can be accepted from the previous signal box under the absolute block system of signalling

Closed circuit television (CCTV) – a television system in which signals are transmitted from a television camera to the receivers by cables or telephone links and used for remote monitoring or supervisory purposes

Coaching stock – vehicles designed to be capable of running in passenger trains

Colour light area – an area in which all signals are of the colour light type and usually worked under the track circuit block system

Colour light signal – a signal that conveys its message by means of coloured lights

Concentrator – a telephone switchboard that allows the signaller to answer or make a call on any one of a number of incoming telephone lines

Control Centre of the Future (CCF) – a computerised system that enables signallers to see on a track diagram on a VDU screen which trains are on time and which are delayed

Controlled signal – a colour light signal that is cleared from red by the signaller and not automatically by the signalling system

Degraded movement – a train movement made without the normal full protection of the signalling system following failure of the equipment. Also called degraded working.

Delay attribution – the process of capturing the causes of delays to trains and identifying the company responsible, e.g. Network Rail or the train operator

Delayed yellow – a signal allowing a train to enter a colour light section without the full overlap distance being available

Detection (points) – a means of ensuring that facing points are correctly closed before the signal can be cleared

Detonator protection – one or more detonators (small disc-shaped devices, placed on the rail head, which explode when a train passes over them) to alert a train driver to an unsafe situation affecting the line ahead, or as part of the protection measures for engineering work on the line

Distant arm proving – a means of ensuring that the distant arm of a semaphore signal is in the 'on' position before the block indicator can be placed to 'line clear'.

Distant signal – a signal that tells the driver whether there is a need to be prepared to stop at the next signal

Double yellow aspect – a preliminary caution signal in four-aspect colour light signalling

Down – all running lines and trains are assigned a direction, either up or down. The up direction is usually towards London.

Driver Advisory System - real-time route information to drivers, helping them to monitor train performance and reliability, and to travel at the optimum train speed

Driver's Reminder Appliance – a device in the driving cab that, when activated, prevents power being taken, enabling the driver to set a reminder that the signal ahead is at danger

Electric token block – a system of signalling used on single lines that permits only one token at a time for a specific section of line to be withdrawn from a token machine. The driver must be in possession of the token before entering the single-line section concerned.

Electronic token – the 'token' used in the Radio Electronic Token Block system

Emergency indicator – a sign used to inform a driver of a speed restriction imposed without prior notice

Emergency replacement switch – a switch that enables the signaller to replace an automatic signal to danger in an emergency

Enhanced permissible speed (EPS) – an increased maximum permissible line speed for trains that can tilt, as indicated by lineside signs

Entrance/exit (NX) – a system of route setting used in power signal boxes whereby to set a route the signaller operates a switch or button at the entrance to the route and at its exit

European Rail Traffic Management System (ERTMS) – a signalling and traffic control system designed to provide a standard system throughout the European Union with Automatic Train Protection inherent within the system

European Train Control System (ETCS) – the signalling part of ERTMS

Examination of the line – a method of establishing whether it is safe to run trains through a section

Facing junction – a junction where a train can take a diverging route depending on the position of the points

Facing points – points (a section of track with moveable rails that can divert a train from one track to another) positioned so that routes for trains passing over them diverge in the normal direction of travel

Fail safe – a term referring to signalling equipment that, in the event of failure or other defect, is designed to fail in a way that does not endanger the safety of train operation

Fixed signal – a signal in a fixed location (the word 'fixed' refers to the location and not to the aspect or indication of the signal)

Flank protection – additional signal and point interlocking at junctions to minimise the possible consequences should a train pass a signal at danger

Flashing yellow aspects – flashing yellow signal lights that warn the driver that the train is routed over a speed-restricted diverging route at a junction ahead

Fouling bar – equipment used to establish that a vehicle is safely clear of a fouling point

Fouling point – the precise spot where a vehicle standing at a converging point between two lines will come into contact with a vehicle on the other line

Four-aspect (signal) – a signal that can display four aspects – red, one yellow, two yellows, or green

Green aspect – a green light indicating that the line ahead is clear and that the next signal will not be at red (or at single yellow in four-aspect signalling)

Ground frame – a raised platform or cabin containing switches or levers for controlling points and signals, but which can only be used when released by the controlling signal box

GSM-R radio – Global System for Mobile Communications – Railway, the radio system that provides the bearer for ETCS and secure communication between drivers and signallers and vice versa

Handshake – the simultaneous successful operation of separate electronic devices in the same system

Handsignaller – a person stationed at the lineside to give signals to the driver by flag or lamp

Headway – the minimum distance between two trains travelling in the same direction that will enable green signals to be given to the driver of the second train and enable it to travel at unrestricted speed

Home normal control (HNC) – a means of ensuring that the home signal lever is replaced in the frame before 'line clear' can be given

Home signal – in absolute block, the first (or outermost) stop signal on the approach to a signal box. May also be called 'outer home' or 'home No 1' where there are two home signals.

Hot axle box detector (HABD) – lineside equipment for detecting an overheated axle box on a rail vehicle

Hudd system (of ATC) – a former system of warning the driver of the need to slow down or stop

Illuminated diagram – a panel in a signal box containing a diagrammatic representation of the track under the signaller's control, with certain functions, such as the location of trains, being shown by lights

Integrated Electronic Control Centre (IECC) – a signalling control centre with visual display units and with routes set by trackerball or keyboard. It incorporates *solid state interlocking* and Automatic Route Setting.

Intermediate block – an additional block section between two absolute block signal boxes generally worked from the rearmost signal box

Isolated – equipment taken out of use

Junction indicator – an attachment to a colour light signal located on the approach to a facing junction that indicates to a driver either by an alphanumeric notation, or by a row of white lights, whether the train is to take a diverging route at the junction

Junction protecting signal – a signal that, if passed at danger, could result in a head-on, a converging, or a crossing collision with a train on the conflicting route

King lever – a lever whose operation unlocks other levers

Light emitting diode (LED) – an electronic device that emits a bright light when energised

Lime Street controls – signalling controls that ensure that a following train will fit into an already occupied platform where permissive working is in force

Line – a loose term that can mean just one pair of rails, e.g. the up line, or all the tracks on a route

Line clear – the position of the block indicator when a signaller has accepted a train

Line speed – the maximum permitted speed of a line

Main aspect – the red, yellow, double-yellow or green aspect of a colour light signal

Manually controlled barrier crossing (MCB) – a level crossing with full barriers that is either operated by the signaller or an approaching train, and must be deemed to be clear of any obstructions before the protecting signal(s) may be cleared

Manual signal box – a signal box in which the levers operating the signals and points are pulled over and replaced by the physical effort of the signaller

Miniature stop lights (MSL) – small red and green lights provided at some types of level crossings. Sometimes referred to as miniature warning lights (MWL).

Modular signalling – lower-cost signalling developed for secondary routes based on a number of standard templates of equipment suitable for specific geographic configurations along the route

Movement authority – on ETCS-fitted lines, the authority transmitted from the Radio Block Centre to the train authorising the driver to proceed to a particular location (the 'end of authority') ahead

Multiple-aspect colour light signals – colour light signals capable of displaying three or four aspects

National Radio Network (NRN) – a legacy radio system that provided a link between driver and signaller, and between the signaller and staff working on the line

Nearside – the left-hand side in the direction of travel

No Signaller Key Token System (NSKT) – a method of working trains over a single line with a signaller at only one end of the section

Normal (of points) – the usual position in which the points lie

NX system – see Entrance/exit system

Obstacle detection – a radar-based system, supplemented by a secondary laser-based system, to detect any obstacles on a manually controlled barrier crossing after the barriers have been lowered

Occupation crossing – a private level crossing on a road that usually allows access between premises and a public road

Occupied – a term used to denote the presence of a train

Off – a proceed aspect in a colour light signal, or a semaphore signal arm inclined at 45°

One control switch system (OCS) – a route-setting signalling system in which a set of points and the junction signal are set by turning the appropriate switch

One train working (OTW) – a method of working a single line in which only one train at a time can be on the line

Open level crossing – a level crossing without gates, barriers or road vehicle stop lights

Out of correspondence – a term denoting that points are not correctly set

Overlap – a section of line beyond a signal that, for safety reasons, must be clear before the previous signal can show a proceed aspect

Override facilities – arrangements at power signal boxes in which (limited) control of the signalling can be obtained in the event of failure of the cable connection between the signal box and remote interlocking(s)

Overspeed sensor – the part of the TPWS system that checks whether the driver is responding appropriately to the caution signal

Permanent speed restriction (PSR) – a speed restriction imposed because of a sharp curve or other permanent feature

Permissive block working – a signalling system that allows more than one train to be in a section on the same line at the same time

PICOP – Person in charge of possession

Pilotman – a person appointed to conduct trains over a single line, or a line being used for trains in both directions, during failure of equipment or repairs, or owing to an obstruction

Platform starting signal – a stop signal at the departure end of a passenger station platform

Position light signal – a signal that authorises shunting or permissive movements. It can either be mounted on the same post as a colour light main signal or can be mounted independently on the ground.

Possession – a period of time that a section of the railway is blocked to service trains so that engineering work can be safely carried out

Power signal box (PSB) – a signal box in which points and signals are operated by electric or other power and controlled by switch or push-button. Interlocking between points and signals is performed by electric relays.

Preliminary Route Indicator (PRI) – a device used in conjunction with junction signalling to give drivers advance information of the direction set for the route ahead in order to avoid misrouting incidents

Proceed aspect – a green, yellow or double yellow light shown at a colour light signal, which means that the driver may proceed past it

Protection of the line – warning action taken to stop trains running into an obstruction, a failed train or other source of danger

Proceed on sight authority (PoSA) – a position light signal that may authorise a driver to proceed even though all the normal safeguards in the route ahead may not be present

Radio Electronic Token Block (RETB) – a signalling system used on single lines in which an electronic token is transmitted to trains

Reading time – in relation to the sighting of signals, the time deemed necessary for a driver to identify the correct signal and understand its meaning

Red aspect – danger, or stop, as displayed by a colour light signal

Remote control system – a system that enables signalling controlled by an interlocking remote from the signal box to be controlled from that signal box

Remote interlocking – interlocking equipment that is not located at the signal box but is controlled from it by means of a remote control system

Repeater – a dial or indicator in a manual signal box showing the position of a signal arm and whether the signal lamp is lit

Replace – the action of changing a stop signal from proceed to stop, or a distant signal from proceed without restriction to caution

Restricted overlap – an overlap shorter than the standard 180 metres, often provided in station areas. When the signal with the restricted overlap is at danger, the previous signal will be maintained at danger until a train is close to it, when it will clear to a single yellow (sometimes called a delayed yellow).

Reverse (of points) – lying in a position opposite to the normal position

Reversed – the position of a lever in a manually operated signal box when it has been pulled over in the frame; the opposite of the normal position

Right away indicator – an indicator that, when illuminated, displays an 'R' or 'RA', indicating to a driver that it is safe to depart from the station

Rightside failure – the failure of signalling equipment to a safe state

Robust train protection – additional signalling controls that have the aim of preventing a train that overruns a junction protecting signal at danger from reaching the junction itself where it would be foul of another train

Route indicator – a form of junction indicator that identifies to a driver by an alphanumeric notation whether the train is to take a diverging route at a junction

Route relay interlocking – a system of interlocking between points and signals performed by electric relays

Route setting – the action by the interlocking of preparing the route ahead, if available, so that the relevant signal can be cleared for a train movement

Ruling gradient – the main or most important gradient on a section of line with more than one gradient

Running line – any line other than a siding. Train movements on running lines are controlled by fixed (running) signals.

Running movement – a normal train movement on a running line, under the control of a running signal

Running signal – a signal that displays main aspects on a running line

Safety critical communications – communications between e.g. a driver and a signaller where, it if it was misunderstood, a dangerous occurrence could occur

Section signal – in absolute block, the stop signal furthest ahead controlled from the same signal box, which admits trains to the section ahead

Semaphore signal – a fixed signal, whose meaning is given to drivers by the position of a rectangular-shaped arm during daylight, and by coloured lights at night

Semi-automatic signal – a colour light signal that is worked automatically by the passage of trains, but which can also be controlled from a signal box or ground frame

Sequential locking – interlocking between signal levers to ensure that they are pulled over in the correct sequence

Service brake application – the normal brake application made by a driver in routine service (as opposed to an emergency application)

Setting back – a short-distance shunting movement, usually in the wrong direction

Shunt ahead signal – a signal that allows a driver to pass a stop signal by a short distance for shunting purposes

Sighting distance – in relation to level crossings, the distance from the crossing when an approaching train first comes into view and can be seen. In relation to signals, the maximum distance at which a driver can see a signal ahead.

Signal assessment tool – a numerical tool used in the assessment of the risk of a signal being passed at danger

Signal post replacement switch – a switch at the foot of an automatic colour light signal that enables the signal to be switched to (and maintained at) red by the use of a key

Signal post telephone – a telephone provided at a signal to enable a driver to speak to a signaller

Signal sighting – the characteristics of a signal relating to the extent to which the driver of an approaching train has sufficient time to identify, observe and interpret the information being displayed by that signal

Signal sighting committee – a group of experts convened to examine the sighting of a signal

Signalling panel – a panel in a signal box giving a diagrammatic representation of the layout under the signaller's control, together with control switches or push-buttons and track circuit, etc, indications

Slotting – a mechanism for controlling semaphore signal arms where two signal boxes are involved

Slow line – a name often used for one of a pair of lines, e.g. the 'up slow line', where there are four lines of way (the other pair being referred to as the fast lines)

Solid-state interlocking – a computerised software system for controlling the interlocking between points and signals

SPAD – signal passed at danger (without authority)

SPAD alarm – a device provided in a signalling centre and triggered if a driver passes a signal at danger without authority

SPAD indicator – a type of signal provided in a few locations where the top and bottom aspects flash red and the centre aspect displays a steady red light if the signal it relates to is passed at danger

SPATE indicator – a sign used to advise drivers of a temporary speed restriction withdrawn earlier than expected or not imposed

Speed indicator – a lineside sign at the start of a permanent or temporary speed restriction advising drivers of the permissible speed ahead

Splitting distants – a form of junction signalling in which the driver is advised of the route ahead by one or more pairs of colour light signals before the junction signal. One colour light signal of each pair is offset from the signal post.

Staff (or train staff) – a form of token used in the working of a single line

Start against signal SPAD (SASSPAD) – an incident of a signal being passed at danger at a platform starting signal

Start on yellow SPAD – an incident of a signal being passed at danger at the first signal ahead of the platform starting signal that was displaying a single yellow aspect

Station limits – the section of line between the outermost home signal and the stop signal furthest ahead worked from the same signal box

Station working – special regulations governing shunting movements within station limits

Stock rail – in a set of points, the rail against which the switch blade fits

Stop signal – a signal capable of showing a stop aspect or indication

Stretcher bars – bars that connect together the switch blades of a set of points, enabling them to move as a pair

Subsidiary signal – in semaphore signalling, a calling-on or shunt ahead signal

Sunflower – driver's name for the AWS visual indicator

Switch blades – the pair of rails that move in a set of points to change the direction of a train. One switch blade fits against the stock rail at each end of the points' travel.

Temporary block working – a method of working following the failure of signalling equipment in which the authority to proceed into the next block section is by a written ticket given to the driver by a handsignaller